THE
FAITH
OF
AMERICA

compiled by:

MORDECAI M. KAPLAN

J. PAUL WILLIAMS

EUGENE KOHN

PRAYERS
READINGS
AND SONGS

FOR THE CELEBRATION OF AMERICAN HOLIDAYS

THE
RECONSTRUCTIONIST PRESS
NEW YORK

CONTENTS

xii

ACKNOWLEDGEMENTS

Acknowledgements

Grateful acknowledgement is hereby made
to the following publishers and authors for
permission to use copyrighted material published or written by them:

Appleton-Century-Crofts, Inc., for "Create Great
Peace," from *War and Laughter*, by James Oppenheim.

Associated Press, for "Now Sing We a Song," from
Fellowship Hymns.

Brandt & Brandt, for excerpts from *We Stand
United*, by Stephen Vincent Benét. Copyright 1942 by
Stephen Vincent Benét. Published by the Walter H.
Baker Company. All performance rights reserved.

Cambridge University Press, for a passage form
Constitutionalism and the Changing World, by C. H.
McIlwain.

Chapman & Grimes, Inc., for an excerpt from *The
Grand Strategy of Evolution*, by William Patten.

Clarendon Press, Oxford, for excerpts from *Sources
and Documents Illustrating the American Revolution*,
edited by Samuel Morison.

Thomas Curtis Clark, for "Build Me A House."

The Colgate-Rochester Divinity School, for excerpts from *Prayers for the New Year*, Vol. XIX, No. 2, of the Colgate-Rochester Divinity School Bulletin.

Collegiate Reformed Protestant Dutch Church of the City of New York, for "Thanksgiving in Hard Times," from a sermon by Edward B. Coe.

Columbia University Press, for an adaptation from "Meditations on the Lives of Nations," by Franklin D. Roosevelt, quoted in *The Roots of American Loyalty*, by Merle Curti.

Doubleday & Company, Inc., for "The Prayer of Columbus" and "Pioneers! O Pioneers!" from *Leaves of Grass*, by Walt Whitman. Copyright 1924 by Doubleday & Company, Inc. For "Trees," from *Trees and Other Poems*, by Joyce Kilmer. Copyright 1914 by Doubleday & Company, Inc. For excerpts from *The New Freedom*, by Woodrow Wilson. Copyright 1913 by Doubleday & Company, Inc.

Duell, Sloan and Pearce, Inc., for excerpts from *America Was Promise*, by Archibald MacLeish. Copyright 1939 by Archibald MacLeish.

E. P. Dutton & Co., Inc., for an adaptation from *Home*, by Kathleen Norris. Copyright 1929 by E. P. Dutton & Co., Inc.

Gaer Associates Inc., for "We Shall Not Be Moved," "United Nations," "Oh Freedom," "Solidarity," "Take This Hammer," and "Union Train," from *The People's Song Book*, edited by W. Hille.

Mrs. J. Borden Harriman, for an excerpt from her sermon *What America Expects of Its Youth.*

John Haynes Holmes for "America Triumphant."

Henry Holt and Company, Inc., for "Prayers of Steel," from *Cornhuskers,* by Carl Sandburg. Copyright 1918 by Henry Holt and Company, Inc. Copyright 1945 by Carl Sandburg.

Houghton Mifflin Company, for "Land That We Love," from *The Great Remembrance: The Poems of Richard Watson Gilder.* For "True Patriotism," from *Letters of Charles Eliot Norton,* edited by Sara Norton and M. A. deWolfe Howe.

The Hymn Society of America, for "Hymn of Patriotism for All Creeds," by M. Willard Lampe.

Charles H. Kerr & Company, for an excerpt from "Addresses on Industrial Unionism," by Eugene V. Debs, New York, Dec. 10, 1905. For an adaptation from "Labor Day Greeting," by Eugene V. Debs, in *Social Democratic Herald,* 1904.

Alfred A. Knopf, Inc., for "A New Wind A-Blowin'," "Slav'ry Chain," "Old Abe Lincoln," "The Liberty Song," "Through All the World," "Johnny Appleseed," "Ode on Science," "Abolitionist Hymn," "Jefferson and Liberty," "Ode to the Fourth of July," and "The Farmer Comes to Town," from *A Treasury of American Song* by Elie Siegmeister and Olin Downes. Copyright 1940, 1943 by Elie Siegmeister and Olin Downes. Music copyright 1940, 1943 by Elie Siegmeister.

Maxim Lieber, for "Let America Be America Again," by Langston Hughes.

Little, Brown & Company and the Atlantic Monthly Press, for an adaptation from the Epilogue to *The Epic of America,* by James Truslow Adams.

Lothrop, Lee & Shepard Co., Inc., for an excerpt from "The Better Way," by Susan Coolidge.

The Macmillan Company, for "On the Building of Springfield," from *General Wm. Booth Enters Heaven,* by Vachel Lindsay. Copyright 1913 by The Macmillan Company. For "Litany of the Heroes," from *Collected Poems,* by Vachel Lindsay. Copyright 1923 by The Macmillan Company. For an excerpt from *The Future of the American Jew,* by Mordecai Kaplan. Copyright 1948 by the Macmillan Company. For an excerpt from *Public Papers and Addresses of Franklin D. Roosevelt.* Vol. 3 & 4. Copyright 1941 by Franklin Delano Roosevelt.

Eward B. Marks Music Corporation, for "Lift Every Voice and Sing." Copyright 1900 by Joseph W. Stern & Co. Renewal copyright 1927 by Edward B. Marks Music Company. Copyright assigned 1932 to Edward B. Marks Music Corporation.

The New York Times, for excerpts from the editorial of June 14, 1940, entitled "Flag Day—1940."

Philosophical Library, Inc., for an adaptation from *The American Way* (selections from the public address of Franklin D. Roosevelt), edited by Dagobert D. Runes.

PREFACE

Preface

NATIONAL HOLIDAYS are designed to call attention to the institutions and ideals that the nation holds sacred. Unfortunately the observance of these days is too often perfunctory. They are treated merely as occasions for recreation. Recreational activity at such times is legitimate, but it has little relation to the purpose which the holidays are intended to serve. Even when they are observed with some measure of public ceremony, their deeper meanings are seldom adequately expressed. A vague and shallow patriotism, devoid of any specific content, is frequently the only sentiment which is evoked.

The purpose of this book is to help give meaning to the most important American holidays by associating them with the ideals appropriate to them, ideals that have gone into the making of the American conscience. Programs for the observance of these holidays are provided, consisting of prayers, readings, and hymns, which can be used by public assemblies, patriotic societies, schools, civic centers, churches, and synagogues to celebrate these holidays in a religious spirit. Such an observance should inspire Americans to view their history and destiny as a part of mankind's striving for goodness, truth, and holiness in human life.

These programs should prove of particular value to interfaith groups. They give a religious interpretation to American history and institutions without reference to the specific doctrines of any of the historic religions with which individual Americans may be affiliated. The programs stress those democratic ideals which make it possible in America for the various religious and racial groups to meet on common ground, for all the great religious traditions that have influenced American life stress the sacredness of human personality, respect for human rights, and the duty of fraternal cooperation for the common welfare.

Each program in this book has the form of a religious service. It begins with an invocation or a message conveying the significance of the day. This is followed by varied selections in prose and poetry, some of them designed for reading by the leader, some for responsive reading by the leader and the assembly, some for silent reading. A few are suggested for choral reading. Interspersed among the readings are hymns and songs, and every program concludes with prayer. It is recommended that an address by a person qualified to relate the message of the day to current social and moral problems be inserted at some appropriate point in the service.

The selections consist in the main of quotations, adaptations, and abridgments of significant passages from American literature and from historic documents of permanent spiritual value. The reason for including passages from historic documents is that they highlight those events which have been influential in inspiring American ideals. In the readings, each holiday is associated with the particular idea that it conveys. What the holidays stand for may be said to constitute the national faith. The following are the holidays for which programs have been provided, with a brief statement of the message each holiday is designed to convey:

1. NEW YEAR'S DAY: a day for the rededication of America to American ideals. The beginning of a new

year suggests the taking of a spiritual inventory of where the nation stands in respect to the fulfillment of its own ideals and traditions. It invites us to a renewal of our devotion to the highest purposes that have been conceived for American life.

2. LINCOLN'S BIRTHDAY: a day devoted to the ideals of equality and fraternity. The career of Abraham Lincoln embodies the ideal of charity to all and malice toward none. His sympathies transcended racial, religious, and sectional differences. His profound reverence for the humanity of all men made him champion their equal right to freedom from oppression and slavery. The observance of his birthday should stress the ideals to which his life was dedicated.

3. WASHINGTON'S BIRTHDAY: a day devoted to the promise and the responsibilities of nationhood. Since Washington presided at the birth of the nation, when as yet it was but the promise of a new and better way of life, the anniversary of his birth should invite reflection on what the nation means to us and to mankind and what it has a right to expect of us.

4. ARBOR DAY: a day devoted to the responsible use of our natural resources. To fail to conserve the natural resources of the nation means to rob its future generations. Arbor Day was instituted to halt the depletion of our arboreal resources through the planting of trees. Its celebration should be dedicated to making us aware of our obligation to use all the ample resources of our country with due regard not only to our own immediate welfare but to that of posterity.

5. MEMORIAL DAY: a day devoted to reflection on sacrifice for American ideals. The solemn remembrance of those who gave their lives that our nation might live should inspire us to see that the nation is worthy of the sacrifices made to preserve it. The observance of Memorial Day should instill a determination to fulfill the ideals on behalf of which those who fell were persuaded to risk their lives.

6. FLAG DAY: a day devoted to reflection on the reality symbolized by the flag. Reverence for the flag is a form of idolatry unless the emotion aroused by the flag is given spiritual significance. The homage paid the flag should be a symbolic expression of allegiance and loyalty to American democratic ideals and the institutions through which they work. It should arouse an appreciation of the values that inhere in our American way of life and of the privilege of sharing in it.

7. INDEPENDENCE DAY: a day devoted to reflection on the uses of freedom. The value of our national independence is determined by the use we make of it. All freedom involves responsibility. Unless used to good advantage it becomes forfeit. Independence Day should be made the occasion for an earnest consideration of how best to use the freedoms we enjoy for the benefit of all our people and of all mankind.

8. LABOR DAY: a day devoted to the reflection on the role of labor in shaping a better world. The dignity of labor arises from the fact that through it man helps to create his own world and to determine the destiny of the human race. But that dignity is present only

when labor is free and is spent voluntarily in meeting the needs of the laborer, his family, and his community. Forced labor and forced idleness alike deprive man of his sacred dignity. Hence Labor Day should stimulate thought on how to render labor as free and creative as we can make it.

9. CONSTITUTION DAY: a day devoted to the American ideal of a government of laws, not of men. The importance of the Constitution that makes the anniversary of its signing an occasion for celebration does not rest primarily on its specific provisions, wise as many of these are. It rests rather on the principle of constitutionalism. That principle means that governmental authority must be defined and limited by law and that the citizen is entitled to know what his rights and his duties are. Constitution Day should inspire us to continue translating into law the ideals of justice and right in human relations.

10. COLUMBUS DAY: a day devoted to an appreciation of the exploring and pioneering spirit. Columbus' daring attempt to reach the East by traveling west opened up a new continent. He was followed by a host of intrepid explorers and pioneers. The pioneering spirit of self-reliance, zest for adventure, and quest for new paths has become a characteristic element of the great American tradition. The observance of Columbus Day should keep alive that spirit and encourage further high adventure in opening up ways of living better than man has yet known.

11. UNITED NATIONS DAY: a day devoted to the ideals of world peace and world unity. National sov-

ereignty does not mean national irresponsibility. Nations, like individuals, are their brothers' keepers. In our world of closely knit economic and cultural ties, no nation can live in isolation; all are interdependent. All must learn to work together to their mutual advantage and to pursue together the welfare of all people everywhere. True to that ideal, the United States assisted at the birth of the United Nations. The anniversary of that event should therefore serve as an occasion for renewing our allegiance to the United Nations and to the ideal of world peace and unity for which it stands.

12. ELECTION DAY: a day devoted to the responsibilities of self-government. The exercise of suffrage is both a sacred right and a solemn responsibility. Election Day should make the citizen aware of his share in government. Its observance should move him to use his ballot conscientiously, to place the public welfare as he sees it above considerations of personal, sectional, or partisan gain.

13. THANKSGIVING DAY: a day devoted to a grateful awareness of the blessings of American life. A blessing not appreciated is easily lost. If we take for granted the blessings that we enjoy by virtue of our living in a land of almost boundless opportunities and take no thought to the moral foundation on which the welfare of our people rests, those blessings will sooner or later be lost. Thanksgiving should be used to make us aware of those moral foundations, of our dependence on divine justice and love for the continued enjoyment of the blessings of American life.

Although the selections in this book are arranged for specific holidays, that arrangement is meant to be suggestive rather than prescriptive. Many of the selections may be used with equal appropriateness for holidays other than those for which they are designated here.

In addition to being used as a sort of liturgy for the public observance of American holidays, the selections in this book can be adapted for use in pageants, dramatizations, and other modes of expression by groups that are willing and able to give sufficient time to such activities.

Thanks are due to the authors and publishers who have permitted us to use material for which they own the copyright. Acknowledgment of our indebtedness to specific authors and publishers will be found on page XVI.

We are indebted to Dr. Ira Eisenstein for his critical reading of the text, to Rabbi Jack J. Cohen and Dr. Joseph Blau for assistance in research, and to Mr. Elie Siegmeister for his advice on the choice of musical material.

This project was initiated by the Jewish Reconstructionist Foundation and was made possible by the generosity of Mr. and Mrs. Joseph Levy, in memory of their daughter, Miriam Levy Finn.

MORDECAI M. KAPLAN
J. PAUL WILLIAMS
EUGENE KOHN

NEW YEAR'S

DAY

A Day for the Rededication of
Americans to American Ideals

The Significance of the Day

O GOD, we have assembled here at the beginning of the new year, to rededicate our lives to the sacred ideals of America. We gratefully acknowledge all that the past year has brought to us and our fellow countrymen of life and health, of love and joy, of beauty and truth, of fortitude and courage. Whatever of good we have known, we recognize as coming from Thee. Therefore are we emboldened, Our Father, to pray for further gifts of Thy grace.

We cannot be contented with ourselves and our achievements, or with the world in which we live—a world in which injustice, cruelty, and deceit hold sway. Disillusioned with ourselves and with our failure to rise to the height of our national ideals in the service of humanity, we entreat Thee to help us fulfill the promise of America.

Give us the courage to be honest: to be true to ourselves and to deal sincerely and forthrightly with our neighbors.

Give us the forbearance that lets live and the love that helps live.

Give us the fortitude to endure the blows of misfortune with serenity.

And when fortune smiles upon us, give us the humility to accept prosperity as Thy gift, to be used in accordance with Thy will.

Help us to build on these shores a free nation of free men. Open our hearts to the truth that every human soul has a worth of its own and must be free to develop that worth to the utmost. Grant that our nation may further the welfare of all its citizens and be of service to them in their pursuit of happiness. Bind all its citizens to the nation and to one another by ties of loyalty. May they ever be willing to share in the nation's enterprise, ever ready to make sacrifices for the good of all. We know that there is no liberty but one: the right, which is also a duty, of making oneself and others free through absolute allegiance to the final goal of man. Keep us aware of all that we owe to our country, that its expectations of us may curb our impulses to do evil and give free rein to our will to do good, for our own true happiness and that of our nation. AMEN.

Rededication to Our Nation's Ideals

THE NEW YEAR invites us to reflect on our nation's past and to rededicate ourselves to its ideals for the future. Our nation was conceived in liberty and dedicated to the faith that all men are equally endowed by their Creator with inalienable rights to life, liberty, and the pursuit of happiness;

> That all men are entitled to use their powers of body and mind in ways that bring joy to them and cause no sorrow to another;

That none shall rule over others except to serve them, that the authority of government shall forever rest on the consent of the governed;

That all who toil shall partake of the full fruit of their toil, and not be deprived of any part of their earnings to satisfy the greed of those who would live by exploiting the labor of others.

Such are the ideals we have inherited from the past, the vision that the best among our people strove to make real in all walks of life.

That vision has inspired our noblest writings, has shaped our most righteous laws, has given the wisest direction to our schools, and has molded our most beneficent institutions.

Let us ever be mindful of the price paid for our freedoms.

Not by mere wishing are visions realized but only by toil and sacrifice.

To the striving for freedom there can be no end until every man, woman, and child has the opportunity to make the most of his life, to employ all his latent powers to his own good and that of his fellow men.

We should, therefore, on this day, explore our shortcomings and raise our sights for the future.

Let us resolve to uproot from our national life every last vestige of bigotry and prejudice, to abolish all unfair discrimination on grounds of race, religion, or national origin.

Let us endeavor to ensure to every worker in his chosen work a free and dignified relation with his employer.

Let us seek to provide all our people with whatever
they need for their health of body and of mind.

> Let us dedicate our schools to the spread of
> knowledge and truth, so that our communities
> may govern themselves with wisdom and under-
> standing.

Let us strive to free men from the tyranny of war,
with its waste, its perils, and its agonies, that the energies of men may be directed to works of peace, to
building a world order based on the mutual helpfulness of men and of nations.

Awareness

God—let me be aware.
Let me not stumble blindly down the ways,
Just getting somehow safely through the days,
Not even groping for another hand,
Not even wondering why it all was planned,
Eyes to the ground unseeking for the light,
Soul never aching for a wild-winged flight.
Please, keep me eager just to do my share.
God—let me be aware.

God—let me be aware.
Stab my soul fiercely with others' pain,
Let me walk seeing horror and stain,
Let my hands, groping, find other hands.
Give me the heart that divines, understands.

Give me the courage, wounded, to fight.
Flood me with knowledge, drench me in light.
Please—keep me eager just to do my share.
God—let me be aware.

—Miriam Teichner

Ring Out, Wild Bells *

Ring out, wild bells, to the wild sky,
   The flying cloud, the frosty light;
   The year is dying in the night;
Ring out, wild bells, and let him die.

Ring out the old, ring in the new,
   Ring, happy bells, across the snow;
   The year is going, let him go;
Ring out the false, ring in the true.

Ring out a slowly dying cause,
   And ancient forms of party strife,
   Ring in the nobler modes of life,
With sweeter manners, purer laws.

Ring out old shapes of foul disease;
   Ring out the narrowing lust of gold;
   Ring out the thousand wars of old,
Ring in the thousand years of peace.

—Alfred Tennyson, In Memoriam

* THE MUSIC FOR THIS POEM IS TO BE FOUND IN *Hymns for the Living Age* (PAGE 87), EDITED BY H. AUGUSTINE SMITH, PUBLISHED BY THE FLEMING H. REVELL COMPANY, NEW YORK.

Penitence for the Nation's Sins

Remember, O my friends, the laws, the rights,
The generous plan of power delivered down
From age to age, by your renowned forefathers.

    O, may it never perish in our hands,
    But may we piously transmit it to our children
    Enriched, enlarged and purified.

And yet, with all the glory of our history,
Are there not moments when we droop in shame
And hang our heads, and sorrow in the knowledge
That, in this mighty land of freedom and free men,
The bodies and souls of little children
Are being dwarfed and broken in our mines,
Our factories and mills, and barred from childhood?

    That there is still a stench of foul corruption,
    In some of our great cities, where legislators
    Are bought and sold, while truth and justice
        suffer?

That rooted in the hearts of men we live with
Abides a rankling hate for fellow humans
Which only sees the light in doing murder?

    That in this fertile land of ours where God
    Created nature's bounties overflowing
    There still remain the naked and the hungry?

Do thou, great Liberty, inspire our souls
To weed out all these old, deep-rooted evils
And make our lives in thy possession happy.

      —*Adapted from Joseph Addison*, CATO,
        and Selden Carlyle Adams, THE UPLIFT

National Characteristics

WE ARE emphatically one people. We all claim a common history, and, whatever be our immediate parentage, are proud to own ourselves the grateful children of the mighty men who declared our country's independence, framed the bond of our Union, and bought with their sacred blood the liberties we enjoy. . . . The nation grew morally strong from its original elements. The great work was delayed only by a just preparation. Now God is bringing hither the most vigorous scions from all the European stocks, to "make of them all *one new* MAN!," not the Saxon, not the German, not the Gaul, not the Helvetian, but the AMERICAN. Here they will unite as one brotherhood, will have one law, will share one interest. Spread over the vast region from the frigid to the torrid zone, from Eastern to Western ocean, every variety of climate giving them choice of pursuit and modification of temperament, the ballot-box fusing together all rivalries, they shall have one national will. What is wanting in one race will be supplied by the characteristic energies of the others; and what is excessive in any, checked by the counter-action of the rest.

—*G. W. Bethune*

Faith in the Future of America

Our voice is not one voice but many voices,
Not one man's, not the greatest, but the people's.

> The blue sky and the forty-eight States of the
>   people,
> Many in easy times, but one in the pinch.

Our voice is all the objectors and dissenters,
And they sink and are lost in the groundswell of the
      people,
Once the people rouse, once the people wake and listen.

> We are the people. Listen to us now.
> Say you we're puny? We built Boulder Dam.

We built Grand Coulee and the T. V. A.
We built them out of freedom and our sweat.

> We made the seas of wheat, the seas of corn.
> We made five States a sea of wheat and corn.

We built the cities and the skyscrapers, but it wasn't
      enough.
We lost our way for a while, but we've found our way.

> We know it and we'll hold it and we'll keep it.
> We'll tell it to the world. We're saying it:

Freedom to speak and pray,
Freedom from want and fear,

Freedom to speak and pray,
Freedom from want and fear—
That's what we're building.

—*Stephen Vincent Benét*, LISTEN TO THE PEOPLE

O God, Who Art the Only Light*

O God, Who art the only light,
Whose Truth lives ever in our sight,
To Thee be praise and singing!
Thy mercy held us in our sleep,
Its never failing watch did keep.

Thy pow'r hath chased dark night away,
And brightly dawns another day,
Thy glorious work revealing.
Thy mercy held us in our sleep
Its never failing watch did keep.

—*Anonymous*

* THE MUSIC FOR THIS SONG IS TO BE FOUND IN *The Ditty Bag,* EDITED AND PUBLISHED BY JANET E. TOBITT, 416 WEST 33RD STREET, NEW YORK.

The Future of America After the
Revolutionary War

At the various turning points of our history,
our fathers were wont to seek their bearings.
They wanted to make sure that the spiritual
wealth acquired at a cost of strain and sacrifice
would not be squandered, that the nation had not
swerved from its goal, but was still true to the
highest purposes to which it was dedicated.
Let us read what Thomas Paine had to say
when the Revolutionary War was over and our
nation was able to settle down to peaceful
pursuits.

THE TIMES THAT TRIED MEN'S SOULS are
over, and the greatest and most complete revolution
the world ever knew, gloriously and happily accomplished.

But to pass from the extremes of danger to safety,
from the tumult of war to the tranquility of peace,
though sweet in contemplation, requires a gradual
composure of the senses to receive it. Even calmness
has the power of stunning, when it opens too instantly
upon us. The long and raging hurricane that should
cease in a moment would leave us in a state rather of
wonder than enjoyment, and some moments of recollection must pass before we could be capable of tasting
the felicity of repose. There are but few instances in
which the mind is fitted for sudden transitions; it takes
in its pleasure by reflection and comparison, and those
must have time to act before the relish for new scenes
is complete.

In the present case, the mighty magnitude of the object, the various uncertainties of fate it has undergone, the numerous and complicated dangers we have suffered or escaped, the eminence we now stand on, and the vast prospect before us, must all conspire to impress us with contemplation.

To see it in our power to make a world happy, to teach mankind the art of being so, to exhibit, on the theatre of the universe, a character hitherto unknown, and to have, as it were, a new creation entrusted to our hands are honors that command reflection and can neither be too highly estimated, nor too gratefully received.

—*Thomas Paine,* THE TIMES THAT TRY MEN'S SOULS

An Ideal for America

What do I desire for my country? How do I vision
the land I love?

Let it be a land where knowledge is free,

Where the mind is without fear, and men hold their
heads high,

Where words come out from the depth of truth,

Where the world has not been broken up into frag-
ments by narrow domestic walls;

13

Where tireless striving stretches its arms toward
   perfection,

Where the clear stream of reason has not lost its way
   in the dreamy desert sand of dead habit,

Where the mind is led forward into ever-widen-
   ing thought and action.

Into that heaven of freedom, my Father, let my country awake.

—Adapted from Rabindranath Tagore, GITANJALI

God Give Us Men

God give us men! A time like this demands
Strong minds, great hearts, true faith, and ready
   hands,
Men whom the lust of office does not kill;
   Men whom the spoils of office cannot buy;
Men who possess opinions and a will;
   Men who have honor; men who will not lie;
Men who can stand before a demagogue
   And damn his treacherous flatteries without wink-
   ing;
Tall men, sun-crowned, who live above the fog
   In public duty and in private thinking;

For while the rabble with their thumb-worn creeds
Their large profession and their little deeds
Mingle in selfish strife, lo! Freedom weeps,
Wrong rules the land, and waiting Justice sleeps.

—*Josiah Gilbert Holland*

Brotherhood Hymn*

When wilt Thou save the people?
Oh God of mercy, when?
Not kings and lords, but nations.
Not thrones and crowns, but men.

Flow'rs of Thy heart, O God, are they;
Let them not pass, like weeds, away,
Their heritage a sunless day,
God save the people.

Shall crime bring crime forever,
Strength aiding still the strong?
Is it Thy will, O Father,
That man shall toil for wrong?

"No," say Thy mountains; "No," Thy skies;
Man's clouded sun shall brightly rise,
And songs be heard instead of sighs;
God save the people.

* THE MUSIC FOR THIS SONG IS TO BE FOUND IN *People's Songs*
(VOLUME 2, NO. II, DECEMBER 1947), A MONTHLY PUBLICA-
TION PUBLISHED BY PEOPLE'S SONGS, NEW YORK.

When wilt Thou save the people?
O God of mercy, when?
The people, Lord, the people,
Not thrones and crowns, but men.

God save the people; Thine they are,
Thy children, as Thy angels fair;
From vice, oppression, and despair,
God save the people.

The One Miracle

I went to call on the Lord in His house on the high hill,
My head full of one-hundred-and-fifty million, having
      to grow up overnight.
"If ever a people, Lord, needed a miracle!"
The Lord He looked at me as a mountain might look
      at a molecule.
"So you want a miracle," said the Lord. "My! My!
      You want a miracle.
I suppose you mean that you want me to come sliding
      down a sunbeam and make one-hundred-and-
      fifty million self-willed egotists overnight
      into one-hundred-and-fifty million coopera-
      tive angels.
Brother," said the Lord, in a voice that shook the
      windows, "That isn't the sort of universe
      you're living in.
And that isn't the sort of God I am."

The room was suddenly vast, with the stars set bright
in the ceiling.
"There is only one miracle," said the Lord.
"All else is cause and effect. All else is law."
The thunder withdrew from the Voice, and the words
came hushed and clear
Like the first stars in the twilight, each star a newborn
glory.
"There is only one miracle, and it is already accom-
plished.
That miracle is the human soul."

The Lord He lifted His head and the Milky Way was
His hair.
"The soul is like the atom," He said. "Wonderfully
like the atom.
Consider the atom.
So minute no lens you can make can enlarge it to a
point where your eye can see it, yet there's a
whole solar system inside it, whirling around
a nucleus like the planets around the sun,
So feeble in its unreleased state, yet actually the great-
est force, save one, in creation,
The greatest force in creation, save one."

The Lord strode through His house so the timbers
whispered to each other,
"He's thinking of the soul tonight, of the soul of man,
And the power asleep in the soul.
He always shakes the house when He thinks of the
power,
The power asleep, asleep in the soul of man."
"I have given you a soul," cried the Lord, "and you
ask Me to come down and do a magician's
trick!

The people who smashed the atom didn't beg Me to
        come with a thunderbolt and split the nu-
        cleus for them.
They knew that there is power in the atom and they
        set to work to release it.
They succeeded, and shook not only New Mexico, they
        shook the world.
All they had to do was to get past the electrons, crack
        the nucleus, and release the power waiting
        to be used.

"There is power in the human soul," said the Lord,
"When you break through and set it free,
Like the power of the atom.
More powerful than the atom,
It can control the atom,
The only thing in the world that can.
I told you that the atom is the greatest force in the
        world, save one.
That one is the human soul.

"But," said the Lord—and the stars in the sky seemed
        to stand still and listen—
"The power must be released, as the atom-breakers re-
        leased the power of the atom.
They had to get past the electrons to get at the energy
        packed in the nucleus.
And I have to get past a deal of ego to release the
        power that is packed in the soul of man.
I keep shooting My rays toward the nucleus,
And the charged field keeps fending them off.
But now and then one gets by,
The nucleus is split, the power is released, and things
        begin to happen on a scale that makes men
        gasp and talk about miracles.

But it isn't a miracle.
It's just the soul of man coming to its own.
It's just the soul of man freed at last to be itself."

The Lord He looked at me and His eyes pierced like
      hot wires.
"Perhaps," He said, "there's something in you and
      numerous others that will have to be cracked
      open, if a hundred-and-fifty million people
      are going to grow up overnight.
Something in you," said the Lord, "something, per-
      haps, in *you*."

That *was* a joke, and I laughed. But the Lord wasn't
      laughing.
I hastened to reassure Him. "There's nothing the mat-
      ter with *me*.
It's the other fellow that's the trouble, a hundred-and-
      fifty million of him."
"I know all about the hundred-and-fifty million," said
      the Lord, and I thought He seemed a little
      tired as He said it, "but I don't at the mo-
      ment seem able to see anyone but you."
"Me, Lord?" I said. "How odd! I'm sure you must be
      mistaken.
There's nothing about me that need give you even a
      moment's uneasiness."

        —*Herman Hagedorn,* THE BOMB THAT FELL
        ON AMERICA

World Democracy

Tragic is the plight of democracy among ourselves and in the world at large:

> Democracy was once a strenuous unity of thought and action; we made of it a way, smooth to the heart's content.

It had been a faith militant and triumphant; we permitted it to disintegrate into a routine of "liberties and comforts." We tried to answer the deepest and most ancient needs of man by developing millions of gadgets and shirking spiritual issues.

> None of us alive today can escape some share of the blame for this; we have all accepted this culture and immersed ourselves in it.

Let us then acknowledge our guilt, not by indulging in maudlin regrets but by seeking immediate atonement.

> We reaffirm that the meaning and goal of human life, for men and for nations, are progress and growth in mind and deed, and that without universal peace there can be no progress or growth;

That peace is indivisible, founded on the unity of man under one law and government;

> That diversity in unity and unity in diversity, as embodied in the structure of our federal union, are destined one day to bring peace to all mankind in a universal democracy.

No one is an American by birthright alone, and the man who is only an American is not yet an American.

But all those are Americans who pledge their lives, their fortunes, and their sacred honor to the creed of a world-embracing democracy, to the fight against the untamed forces of Hate and Evil that keep men asunder.

They are Americans whether they claim an American ancestry of centuries or whether they themselves landed from Mayflowers of hope and will.

We all call fatherland the distant lands whence we or our ancestors fled from injustice and bondage.

Of this country we know that its intimate name is the City of Brotherly Love.

We know that out of it and of all fading fatherlands, one Brotherland must be made—the City of Man.

We know that the United States must be the Uniting States.

—*Suggested by Herbert Agar, Frank Aydelotte, G. A. Borgese, and others,* THE CITY OF MAN

A New Wind A-Blowin'*

There's a brand new wind a-blowin' down that Lincoln road

There's a brand new hope a-growin' down where freedom's seeds are sowed
There's a new truth we'll be knowin' that will lift our
 heavy load
When we find out what free men can really do.

There's a brand new day a'comin' for the land called
 U. S. A.
New tunes we'll be a strummin' in our hearts by night
 and day.
As we march on we'll be hummin' how our trouble's
 gone away
'Cause we've found out what free men can really do.

And if you feel like dancin' then, why come on folks,
 and dance!
And if you feel like prancin' then, why come on folks,
 and prance!
'Cause I really ain't romancin' when I say we've got
 our chance
To show 'em what free men can really do.

There's a brand new wind a-blowin' thru a land that's
 proud and free.
Ev'rywhere there's folks a-wakin' to a truth that's
 bound to be
So let's all pull together for that day of victory,
And we'll show 'em what free men can really do!

—*Langston Hughes*

* THE MUSIC FOR THIS SONG IS TO BE FOUND IN *A Treasury of
American Song* (SECOND EDITION, PAGE 405), EDITED BY OLIN
DOWNES AND ELIE SIEGMEISTER, PUBLISHED BY ALFRED A.
KNOPF, INC., NEW YORK.

The Ideals of Our American Democracy

THERE IS A DEEPER SOURCE of love of country than the material advantages and benefits it may afford. It is in the character of its people, in their moral life, in the type of civilization which they exhibit. The elements of human nature are indeed so fixed that favorable or unfavorable circumstances have little effect upon its essential constitution, but prosperity or the reverse brings different traits into prominence. The conditions which have prevailed in America have, if broadly considered, tended steadily and strongly to certain good results in the national character; not, indeed, to unmixed good, but to a preponderance of good. The institutions established for self-government have been founded with intent to secure justice and independence for all. The social relations among the whole body of the people are humane and simple. The general spirit of the people is liberal, is kindly, is considerate. The ideals for the realization of which, in private and public conduct, there is more or less steady and consistent effort, are as high and as worthy as any which men have pursued. Every genuine American holds to the ideal of justice for all men, of independence, including free speech and free action within the limits of law, of obedience to law, of universal education, of material well-being for all the well-behaving and industrious, of peace and good-will among men. These, however far short the nation may fall in expressing them in its actual life, are—no one will deny it—the ideals of our American democracy.

—*Charles Eliot Norton,* TRUE PATRIOTISM

Wassail Song*

*New Year's Day evokes many solemn thoughts,
but it also suggests faith, hope, and confidence in
the joyous possibilities of life. That mood is reflected in the following folk song, which was sung
by groups who went from house to house to make
merry with their neighbors in the manner described.*

Here we come a-wassailing
Among the leaves so green,
Here we come a-wand'ring,
So fair to be seen:

CHORUS
Love and joy come to you,
And to you your wassail too,
And God bless you, and send you a
            Happy New Year,
And God send you a Happy New Year.

We are not daily beggars
That beg from door to door,
But we are neighbors' children
Whom you have seen before.

CHORUS

* THE MUSIC FOR THIS SONG IS TO BE FOUND IN *Fireside Book
of Folksongs,* EDITED BY MARGARET BRADFORD BONI, PUBLISHED
BY SIMON & SCHUSTER, INC., NEW YORK.

Our wassail cup is made
Of the rosemary tree,
And so is your beer
Of the best barley.

We have got a little purse
Of stretching leather skin;
We want a little of your money
To line it well within.

CHORUS

God bless the master of this house,
Likewise the mistress too;
And all the little children
That round the table go.

CHORUS

—*Anonymous*

Closing Prayer

O Eternal God of ages past and ages yet to come,
Thou who art the everlasting Togetherness, the never-
      dimming Light, the ever-fulfilling Love,
Whose breath is the Surge of Life, whose pulse is
      Eternal Creation,
Open Thou the curtains of time for a new year's un-
      folding.

Lead us to the threshold of things yet unborn.

Make us malleable to learn, flexible to discern, humble
      in seeking.

Teach us, O God, to see beneath surfaces,

To look beyond small horizons, to rise above triviali-
      ties.

Be as a mighty sieve to sift us, as the blazing search-
      light to brighten the way.

From out of solitude weld us into eternal Fellowship.

From out of complacency stir in us divine discontent.

But from out of fear restore in us the peace of hum-
      ble striving.

Out of sheer dreams bring us enduring visions.

Out of deadly routine point us to pressing purpose.

Out of weakness grant us strength.

Out of indecision bring us guided resolution.

Out of impasse show us direction.

Find us and fathom us; free us; fulfill us; fire our imag-
      inations.

Prepare in us Thy divine anticipation, that we may lay
      hold of those priceless treasures that are so
      easily missed, so silently lost.

Chasten us but strengthen us;

Replenish us; renew us;

Transform us now and never ceasingly, that Thy will
      be done. AMEN.

—Faculty of Colgate Divinity School,
PRAYERS OF THE NEW YEAR

26

FEBRUARY 12

LINCOLN'S

BIRTHDAY

A Day Devoted to the Ideals
of Equality and Fraternity

The Significance of the Day

THIS DAY is gratefully dedicated to the remembrance of Abraham Lincoln, who led the United States through four years of civil strife to keep the nation one, and who used the power of his office to free the Negroes from slavery. His memory is both an inspiration and a challenge. It inspires us to dedicate our lives as he did his, to freeing the bound. It challenges us to make of our country a land in which all men are accepted by their fellow men for what they are and for what they can make of themselves.

We are wont in family life to accept our brother; we assume his right to be himself, to seek his own welfare in his own way; we ask of him only that he share with us a common devotion to the family. So let us in our public life accept our fellow man in brotherhood. Let us acknowledge his right to his own interests, his own beliefs, his own loyalties. Let us ask of him only that he share with us a common devotion to the cause of all humanity.

Ours is a nation built by men of different races, different faiths, different cultural traditions. To recognize all of them as our brothers is to show respect for their right to be different from us. It is to learn to value the special contribution which each can bring to the common cause. It is to welcome his cooperation in the building of a common civilization. That civilization should be great enough to embrace all the diversities among us. Let us make America safe for differences and liberate all those who today are oppressed by unbrotherly prejudice and rancor. Thus and thus only can we honor the memory of Abraham Lincoln and bring victory to the cause for which he lived and died.

Slav'ry Chain*

CHORUS
Slav'ry chain done broke at las',
Broke at las', broke at las',
Slav'ry chain done broke at las',
Goin' to praise God 'till I die.

Oh, mah Lawd, how I did suffer
In de dungeon and de chains;
And de days I went wif head bowed down
And my broken flesh an' pain
(But brethren)

CHORUS

—Anonymous

*THE MUSIC FOR THIS SONG IS THAT OF "JOSHUA FIT DE BATTLE OF JERICHO" AND IS TO BE FOUND IN *A Treasury of American Song* (SECOND EDITION, PAGE 194), EDITED BY OLIN DOWNES AND ELIE SIEGMEISTER, PUBLISHED BY ALFRED A. KNOPF, INC., NEW YORK.

The Dream of a United People

People, you people, living everywhere . . .
People, who live at postmarks with queer names
People whose contour plows bring back the grass
To a dust-bitten and dishonored earth,
And those who farm the hillside acres still
And raise up fortitude between the stones,
Millions in cities, millions in the towns . . .
All races and all stocks, all creeds and cries,
And yet one people, one, and always striving . . .
Out of the flesh, out of the minds and hearts
Of thousand upon thousand common men,
Cranks, martyrs, starry-eyed enthusiasts,
Slow-spoken neighbors, hard to push around,
Women whose hands were gentle with their kids
And men with a cold passion for mere justice,
We make this thing, this dream.

    This land unsatisfied by little ways,
    This peaceless vision, groping for the stars,

Not as a huge devouring machine
Rolling and clanking with a remorseless force
Over submitted bodies and the dead,
But as live earth where anything could grow,
Your crankiness, my notions, and his dreams,
Grow and be looked at, grow and live or die,
But get their chance of growing and the sun.

    We made it and we make it and it's ours.
    We shall maintain it. It shall be sustained.

—*Stephen Vincent Benét,* WE STAND UNITED

Abe Lincoln*

Abe Lincoln had an Illinois face,
And he came out of a pioneer race.
He knew how hard the fight would be,
And he liked the idea of being free.

His heart was tough as a railroad tie,
He was made of stuff that doesn't die.
He was made of hopes, he was made of fears,
He was made to last a million years.

Freedom's a thing that has no ending,
It needs to be cared for, it needs defending.
Freedom!

—*Earl Robinson and Millard Lampell,*
THE LONESOME TRAIN

*THE MUSIC FOR THIS SONG IS TO BE FOUND IN *The Lonesome Train* (PAGES 89-93), BY EARL ROBINSON AND MILLARD LAMPELL, PUBLISHED BY THE SUN MUSIC COMPANY, 50 WEST 57TH STREET, NEW YORK.

The Voice of Abraham Lincoln

We observe the anniversary of Abraham Lincoln's birth because we want never to forget his message to our people. Let us then reverently read some of the words addressed by Lincoln to his contemporaries which retain their validity for us.

EVERY MAN is said to have his peculiar ambition. Whether it be true or not, I can say, for one, that I have no other so great as that of being truly esteemed of my fellow-men, by rendering myself worthy of their esteem.

We find ourselves in the peaceful possession of the fairest portion of the earth as regards extent of territory, fertility of soil, and salubrity of climate. We find ourselves under the government of a system of political institutions conducing more essentially to the ends of civil and religious liberty than any of which the history of former times tells us. We, when mounting the stage of existence, found ourselves the legal inheritors of these fundamental blessings. We toiled not in the acquirement or establishment of them; they are a legacy bequeathed us by a once hardy, brave, and patriotic, but now lamented and departed, race of ancestors. Theirs was the task—and nobly they performed it—to possess themselves, and through themselves us, of this goodly land, and to uprear upon its hills and its valleys a political edifice of liberty and equal rights; 'tis ours only to transmit these—the

33

former unprofaned by the foot of an invader, the latter undecayed by the lapse of time and untorn by usurpation—to the latest generation that fate shall permit the world to know. This task, gratitude to our fathers, justice to ourselves, duty to posterity, and love for our species in general, all imperatively require us faithfully to perform.

Most governments have been based practically on the denial of the equal rights of men; . . . ours began by affirming those rights. They said, some men are too ignorant and vicious to share in government. Possibly so, said we; and by your system you would always keep them ignorant and vicious. We proposed to give all a chance; and we expected the weak to grow stronger; the ignorant, wiser; and all better and happier together.

We made the experiment; and the fruit is before us. Look at it—think of it. Look at it in its aggregate grandeur, of extent of country and numbers of population—of ship, and steamboat, and trail.

"A house divided against itself cannot stand." I believe this government cannot endure permanently half slave and half free. I do not expect the Union to be dissolved—I do not expect the house to fall—but I do expect it will cease to be divided. It will become all one thing, or all the other. Either the opponents of slavery will arrest the further spread of it, and place it where the public mind shall rest in the belief that it is in the course of ultimate extinction; or its advocates will push it forward till it shall become alike lawful in all the States, old as well as new, North as well as South.

34

From the first appearance of man upon the earth down to very recent times, the words "stranger" and "enemy" were quite or almost synonymous. Even yet, this has not totally disappeared. The man of the highest moral cultivation, in spite of all which abstract principle can do, likes him whom he does know much better than him whom he does not know. To correct the evils, great and small, which spring from want of sympathy and from positive enmity among strangers, as nations or as individuals, is one of the highest functions of civilization.

This is a world of compensation; and he who would be no slave must consent to have no slave.

Hymn of Patriotism for All Creeds*

God of our history,
Our fathers worshiped Thee
With one accord.
They were from many lands,
Of many creeds and clans,
But Thee, with lifted hands,
They all adored!

God of our present hour,
Send forth Thy saving power
In this our day:

* TO BE SUNG TO THE TUNE OF "AMERICA."

Grant us the grace to see,
In our diversity,
The bond of unity,
    Father, we pray.

Blend Thou our liberty
With true fraternity
    The World around.
Till every land be free
To trust not only Thee
But all humanity,
    And peace abound.

God of our destiny,
Be this old litany
    Our staff and rod:
"Do justly" while we may,
"Love mercy" day by day,
"Walk humbly" all the way
    With Thee our God!

—*Millard Lampell*

The Emancipation Proclamation

The crowning achievement of Abraham Lincoln's career was the emancipation of the Negro slave. That emancipation was not achieved at one stroke. Indeed, there is still much that remains to be done before the Negro can be said to enjoy the same freedom of opportunity as the white man. The great initial step, however, in the liberation of the Negro from slavery was the Emancipation Proclamation. Let us read the salient portions of that proclamation.

WHEREAS, on the twenty-second day of September, in the year . . . one thousand eight hundred and sixty-two, a proclamation was issued by the President of the United States, containing, among other things, the following, to wit:

"That on the first day of January, in the year . . . one thousand eight hundred and sixty-three, all persons held as slaves within any state, or designated part of a State, the people whereof shall then be in rebellion against the United States, shall be then, thenceforward, and forever free."

Now, therefore, I, Abraham Lincoln, President of the United States, by virtue of the power in me vested as commander-in-chief of the army and navy of the United States, in time of actual armed rebellion against the authority and government of the United States, and as a fit and necessary war measure for suppressing said rebellion, . . . do order and declare that all persons held as slaves within said designated States and parts of States are, and henceforward shall be, free; and that the Executive Government of the United

States, including the military and naval authorities thereof, will recognize and maintain the freedom of said persons.

And I hereby enjoin upon the people so declared to be free to abstain from all violence, unless in necessary self-defence; and I recommend to them that, in all cases when allowed, they labor faithfully for reasonable wages.

And I further declare and make known that such persons of suitable condition will be received into the armed service of the United States to garrison forts, positions, stations, and other places, and to man vessels of all sorts in said service.

And upon this act, sincerely believed to be an act of justice, warranted by the Constitution upon military necessity, I invoke the considerate judgment of mankind and the gracious favor of Almighty God.

Constitutional Amendments
Emancipating the Negro

The Emancipation Proclamation was a war measure. Its application was limited to those states that had seceded from the Federal Union. The actual abolition of slavery and the civil and political emancipation of the Negro were effected by the adoption of the Thirteenth, Fourteenth, and Fifteenth Amendments to the Constitution, which read, in part, as follows.

AMENDMENT XIII

Section 1. Neither slavery nor involuntary servitude, except as a punishment for crime, whereof the party shall have been duly convicted, shall exist within the United States, or any place subject to their jurisdiction.

Section 2. Congress shall have power to enforce this article by appropriate legislation.

AMENDMENT XIV

Section 1. All persons born or naturalized in the United States, and subject to the jurisdiction thereof, are citizens of the United States, and of the State wherein they reside. No State shall make or enforce any law which shall abridge the privileges or immunities of citizens of the United States. Nor shall any State deprive any person of life, liberty or property without due process of law, nor deny to any person within its jurisdiction the equal protection of the laws.

AMENDMENT XV

Section 1. The right of citizens of the United States to vote shall not be denied or abridged by the United

States or by any State, on account of race, color or previous condition of servitude.

Go Down Moses*

Go down, Moses,
'Way down in Egypt land,
Tell ole Pharaoh, to let My people go.
Go down, Moses, 'way down in Egypt land,
Tell ole Pharaoh, to let My people go.
When Israel was in Egypt land,
Let My people go,
Oppressed so hard they could not stand,
Let My people go.

"Thus spoke the Lord," bold Moses said:
Let My people go.
If not I'll smite your first born dead,
Let My people go.

Go down, Moses,
'Way down in Egypt land,
Tell ole Pharaoh, to let My people go.
O let My people go.

—Anonymous

* THE MUSIC FOR THIS SONG IS TO BE FOUND IN *The Books of American Negro Spirituals* (VOLUME 50, PAGE 51), EDITED BY J. W. JOHNSON AND J. ROSAMOND JOHNSON, PUBLISHED BY THE VIKING PRESS, NEW YORK.

The Responsibility of Citizenship in a Democracy

Silent Meditation

I MYSELF am a part of democracy—I myself must accept responsibility. Democracy is not merely a privilege to be enjoyed—it is a trust to keep and maintain. When by idle word and vain prejudice, I create distrust of democracy itself, by so much do I diminish all democracy. When I tell my children that all politics is a rotten machine and all politicians thieves and liars, by so much do I shake their faith in the world that they too must build. When I let loose intolerance, whether it be of race, creed or class, I am letting loose a tiger. When I spend my time vilifying and abusing a duly-elected government of the people because I did not vote for it, by so much do I weaken confidence in government by the people itself. Rich or poor, young or old, Republican or Democrat, I cannot afford these things.

I cannot afford them because there are forces loose in the world that would wipe all democracy out. They will take my idle words and make their own case with them. They will take my halfhearted distrust, and with it sow, not merely distrust, but disunion. They will take my hate and make of it a consuming fire.

I am an American. I intend to stay an American. I will do my best to wipe from my heart hate, rancor and political prejudice. I will sustain my government. And, through good days or bad, I will try to serve my country.

—*Stephen Vincent Benét*, WE STAND UNITED

For a Rededication of America to Her Traditional Ideals

Let America be America again.
Let it be the dream it used to be.

> Let it be the pioneer on the plain
> Seeking a home where he himself is free.

Let America be the dream the dreamers dreamed—
Let it be that great strong land of love,

> Where never kings connive nor tyrants scheme
> That any man be crushed by one above.

O, let my land be a land where Liberty
Is crowned with no false patriotic wreath,

> But opportunity is real, and life is free,
> Equality is in the air we breathe.

O, let America be America again—
The land that never has been yet—
And yet must be—the land where *every* man is free,

> The land that's mine—the poor man's, Indian's,
>   Negro's—we
> Who made America,
> Whose sweat and blood, whose faith and pain,
> Whose hand at the foundry, whose plow in the
>   rain,
> Must bring back our mighty dream again.

And yet this oath I swear—
America will be!
Out of the rack and ruin of our gangster death,
The rape and rot of graft, and stealth, and lies,
We, the people, must redeem America.

We, the people, must redeem
The land, the mines, the plants, the rivers,
The mountains and the endless plain—
All, all the stretch of these great green states—
And make America America again!

—Langston Hughes,
LET AMERICA BE AMERICA AGAIN

The American Promise

Recommended for choral reading

O my America for whom?
For whom the promises? For whom the river?
"It flows west! Look at the ripple of it!"
The grass, "so that it was wonderful to see
And endless, without end with wind wonderful!"
The Great Lakes: Landless as oceans; their beaches
Coarse sand: clean gravel; pebbles;
Their bluffs smelling of sunflowers: smelling of surf:
Of fresh water: of wild sunflowers . . . wilderness.
For whom the evening mountains on the sky;
The night wind from the west; the moon descending?

43

The promises were Man's: the land was his—
Man endowed by his Creator:
Earnest in love: perfectible by reason:
Just and perceiving justice: His natural nature
Clear and sweet at the source as springs in trees are.
It was Man the promise contemplated.
The times had chosen Man; no other:
Bloom on his face of every future:
Brother of stars and of all travelers:
Brother of time and of all mysteries:
Brother of grass also of fruit trees.
It was Man who had been promised: who should have.
Man was to ride from the Tidewater: over the Gap:
West and South with the water: taking the book with
      him:
Taking the wheat seed: corn seed: pip of apple:
Building liberty a farmyard wide:
Breeding for useful labor: for good looks:
For husbandry: humanity: for pride—
Practising self-respect and common decency.

      —*Archibald MacLeish,* AMERICA WAS PROMISES

The Triumph of Freedom

God speed the year of jubilee,
  The wide world o'er!
When, from their galling chains set free,
The oppressed shall vilely bend the knee
And wear the yoke of tyranny,
  Like brutes, no more:—

That year will come, and Freedom's reign
To man his plundered rights again
    Restore.

God speed the day when human blood
Shall cease to flow!
In every clime be understood
The claims of Human Brotherhood,
And each return for evil, good—
Not blow for blow:—

    That day will come, all feuds to end,
    And change into a faithful friend
        Each foe.

God speed the hour, the glorious hour,
When none on earth
Shall exercise a lordly power,
Nor in a tyrant's presence cower,
But all to Manhood's stature tower,
By equal birth!
Until that year, day, hour arrive,—
If life be given,—
With head and heart and hand we'll strive
To break the rod, to rend the gyve,
The spoiler of his prey deprive,—
So witness heaven!

    And never from our chosen post,
    Whate'er the peril or the cost,
        Be driven.

                —*William Lloyd Garrison*

The Battle Hymn of the Republic

Mine eyes have seen the glory of the coming of the
    Lord;
He is trampling out the vintage where the grapes of
    wrath are stored;
He hath loosed the fateful lightning of His terrible
    swift sword;
His truth is marching on.

CHORUS
Glory! glory! Hallelujah!
Glory! glory! Hallelujah!
Glory! glory! Hallelujah!
His truth is marching on.

I have seen Him in the watchfires of a hundred circling
    camps;
They have builded Him an altar in the evening dews
    and damps;
I can read His righteous sentence by the dim and flar-
    ing lamps.
His day is marching on.
CHORUS

He has sounded forth the trumpet that shall never call
    retreat;
He is sifting out the hearts of men before His judg-
    ment seat;
Be swift, my soul, to answer Him! be jubilant my feet!
Our God is marching on.
CHORUS

—*Julia Ward Howe*

46

Closing Prayer

GOD OF THE FREE, we pledge our hearts and lives today to the cause of all mankind.

Grant us victory over the tyrants who would enslave all free men and nations. Grant us faith and understanding to cherish all those who fight for freedom, as if they were our brothers. Grant us brotherhood in hope and union for all the days to come which shall and must unite all the children of earth.

Our earth is but a small star in the great universe. Yet of it we can make, if we choose, a planet unvexed by war, untroubled by hunger or fear, undivided by senseless distinctions of race, color, or theory. Grant us that courage and foreseeing to begin this task today, that our children and our children's children may be proud of the name of man.

The spirit of man has awakened and the soul of man has gone forth. Grant us the wisdom and the vision to comprehend the greatness of man's spirit, that suffers and endures so hugely for a goal beyond his own brief span. Grant us honor for the dead who died in the faith, honor for our living who work and strive for the faith, redemption and security for all captive lands and people. Grant us patience with the deluded and pity for the betrayed. And grant us the skill and the valor that shall cleanse the world of oppression, of the old base doctrine that the strong must eat the weak because they are strong.

Yet most of all grant us brotherhood, not only for this day but for all our years—a brotherhood not of words but of acts and deeds. We are all of us children of earth—grant us that simple knowledge. If our brothers are oppressed, then we are oppressed. If they hunger, we hunger. If their freedom is taken away, our freedom is not secure. Grant us a common faith that man shall know bread and peace, that he shall know justice and righteousness, freedom and security, an equal chance to do his best, not only in our own land, but throughout the world. And in that faith let us march toward the clean world our hands can make. AMEN.

—*Stephen Vincent Benét*

WASHINGTON'S

BIRTHDAY

A Day Devoted to the Promise and
the Responsibility of Nationhood

The Significance of the Day

ON THIS DAY, sacred to the memory of George Washington, we gratefully renew our loyalty to our nation, of which he was the foremost founder. We re-dedicate ourselves to the cause of national freedom, a cause to which he remained steadfast through peril, hardship, treachery, and disaster, until victory was won and the new nation safely launched.

God grant that this day arouse in us the will to make of this nation the best that it can become, to justify the faith which the Founding Fathers reposed in it. May the ample resources with which nature has blessed our country nurture a nation of men and women strong, self-reliant, generous, and free. May the government which its people set up ever protect their liberties, advance their welfare, shield them against disloyalty from within and aggression from without. May it establish just and friendly relations between us and all the other peoples of the world. May the citizens of our country ever live together in mutual trust and good will. May they know the joy of creative labor in farm and in workshop, in studio and laboratory. Be theirs a religious faith free from bigotry and superstition, a piety that cherishes all things good and gracious which glorify the Source of all life. AMEN.

Washington, the Father of His Country

MANY WERE THE MEN who helped to found the United States of America. There were those who fought the Revolutionary War, those who led the Sons of Liberty, those who gave thought to the needs of their countrymen, and those who taught what it meant to become independent. There were Samuel Warren, Samuel Adams, Paul Revere, Ethan Allen, Thomas Paine, Alexander Hamilton, John Adams, Thomas Jefferson, and many others.

> Let us honor their names and celebrate them through the years.

Yet there was one who, above all these, bore the title "Father of His Country,"

> George Washington, acclaimed "first in war, first in peace, and first in the hearts of his countrymen."

Washington was not a warrior by choice, though he led the tattered army of revolutionists to victory over the mighty power of England. He was not a statesman by choice, though he steered the infant country through eight perilous years. He was slow of speech and of thought, endlessly and tirelessly patient when the going was hardest. He was not a romantic hero and he did not quicken men's pulses.

> Yet Washington remains for us, as he was for earlier generations, the symbol of the making of our nation through the shared perils of war and the shared achievements of peace.

The remembrance of his devoted leadership should not only evoke in us sentiments of patriotic pride; it should also hold forth to us a standard of leadership.

We need in every age leaders of integrity and courage, swayed not by passion, prejudice, and self interest but by reason, fairness, and deep concern for the common good.

In our day, as in the days of our first president, we have but recently emerged from the ordeal of war and are faced with new tasks and unprecedented responsibilities.

It is for us to forge so just and honorable a peace that within our nation, and between us and other nations, mutual suspicions and fears will be assuaged and concord and cooperation prevail.

God grant that our country be blessed with a leadership that will help it to fulfill the promise of its beginning,

The promise of a free society that would enable all men to bring their highest powers to fruition, to achieve a full measure of health, wisdom, goodness, and happiness.

May the fidelity of all of us, leaders and followers alike, to all that is best in the American way of life win for us the friendship and good will of all the peoples of the world,

That the promise of America may become the promise of mankind, and that its fulfillment may usher in the longed-for era of universal peace, freedom, and brotherhood.

Hail, Columbia!

Hail, Columbia, happy land!
Hail, ye heroes, heav'n born band!
Who fought and bled in freedom's cause,
Who fought and bled in freedom's cause,
And when the storm of war was gone,
Enjoyed the peace your valor won.
Let independence be our boast,
Ever mindful what it cost,
Ever grateful for the prize;
Let its altar reach the skies.

CHORUS
Firm, united, let us be,
Rallying round our liberty!
As a band of brothers joined,
Peace and safety we shall find.

Behold the chief who now commands,
Once more to serve his country, stands,
The rock on which the storm will beat!
The rock on which the storm will beat!
But armed in virtue, firm and true,
His hopes are fixed on heav'n and you.
When hope was sinking in dismay,
When gloom obscured Columbia's day,
His steady mind from changes free,
Resolv'd on death or liberty.

—*Joseph Hopkinson*

The Spiritual Foundation
of Our National Life

On retiring from the presidency, George Washington, in his farewell address, left his country a legacy of wise counsel. The following passage reveals what he regarded as the spiritual foundation on which our national life should be built.

OF ALL THE DISPOSITIONS and habits which lead to political prosperity, religion and morality are indispensable supports. In vain would that man claim the tribute of patriotism who should labor to subvert these great pillars of human happiness—these firmest props of the duties of men and citizens. The mere politician, equally with the pious man, ought to respect and to cherish them. A volume would not trace all their connections with private and public felicity. Let it simply be asked, Where is the security for property, for reputation, for life, if the sense of religious obligation *desert* the oaths which are the instruments of investigation in courts of justice? And let us with caution indulge the supposition that morality can be maintained without religion. Whatever may be conceded to the influence of refined education on minds of peculiar structure, reason and experience both forbid us to expect that national morality can prevail in exclusion of religious principle. . . .

Observe good faith and justice toward all nations. Cultivate peace and harmony with all. Religion and morality enjoin this conduct. And can it be that good policy does not equally enjoin it? It will be worthy of a free, enlightened and at no distant period a great nation to give to mankind the magnanimous and too novel example of a people always guided by an exalted justice and benevolence. Who can doubt that, in the course of time and things, the fruits of such a plan would richly repay any temporary advantages which might be lost by a steady adherence to it? Can it be that Providence has not connected the permanent felicity of a nation with its virtue?

These Things Shall Be *

These things shall be; a loftier race
    Than e'er the world hath known shall rise,
With flame of freedom in their souls
    And light of knowledge in their eyes.

They shall be gentle, brave, and strong
    To spill no drop of blood, but dare
All that may plant man's lordship firm
    On earth, and fire, and sea, and air.

Nation with nation, land with land,
    Unarmed shall live as comrades free;
In every heart and brain shall throb
    The pulse of one fraternity.

—*John Addington Symonds*

* THE MUSIC FOR THIS POEM IS TO BE FOUND IN *Girl Scouts Song Book,* PUBLISHED BY THE NATIONAL GIRL SCOUTS OF AMERICA.

America Marches On

From what the tyrants rejected, we have built a joyous
    nation!
We have grown rich with her mighty wealth, filled
    with her gracious bounty.
We have known Contentment, Comfort, Security.
And now, one hundred and fifty million strong, we
    come marching,

    Our arms and hearts laden with the wealth and
        strong with the strength she has given us
    One hundred and fifty million people who have
        vowed that she shall stand,

One hundred and fifty million brains, three hundred
    million hands!
All grateful and sure, determined and firm.

    With all of the might of her,
    And all of the right of her,
    America marches on!

From what the tyrants rejected we have built a joyous
    nation,
Flinging its great towers into the sky,

    Raising a race who will defend the rights of man
    Against the wrongs of any man.

In the continent there before you
The fields yield up their abundance,
The earth pours out its oil and ore.

From a thousand factories come silver-winged
    ships,
And from a thousand smelters, the flame soars
    high.

Everywhere, everywhere with all of the wealth of her,
All of the might of her, all of the right of her,
America rises at last vital and strong.

America rises at last, vital and strong,
The mother of nations, to make all men free.

            —*William A. Bacher* (ed.),
            TREASURY STAR PARADE

Meditation on the Lives of Nations

LIVES OF NATIONS are determined, not by the
count of years, but by the life-time of the human spirit.
The life-time of man is three-score years and ten; a
little more, a little less. The life of a nation is the fullness of the measure of its will to life. A nation, like a
person, has a body—a body that must be fed and
clothed and housed, invigorated and rested, in a manner that measures up to the standards of our time.
A nation, like a person, has a mind—a mind that must
be kept informed and alert, that must know itself, that
understands the hopes and needs of its neighbors—

all the other nations that live within the narrowing circle of the world. A nation, like a person, has something deeper, something more permanent, something larger than the sum of all its parts. It is that something which matters most to the future, which calls for the most sacred guarding of its present.

—*Franklin D. Roosevelt*

The Toast to General Washington*

'Tis Washington's health—fill a bumper all round,
For he is our glory and pride.
Our arms shall in battle with conquest be crowned,
Whilst virtue and he's on our side.

'Tis Washington's health—loud cannons should roar,
And trumpets the truth should proclaim:
There cannot be found, search all the world o'er,
His equal in virtue and fame.

'Tis Washington's health—our hero to bless,
May heaven look graciously down:
Oh! long may he live, our hearts to possess,
And freedom still call him her own.

—*Francis Hopkinson*

* THE MUSIC FOR THIS SONG IS TO BE FOUND IN *Landmarks of Early American Music,* EDITED BY RICHARD FRANKO GOLDMAN AND ROGER SMITH, PUBLISHED BY G. SCHIRMER, INC., NEW YORK.

The Universality of the American Spirit

My country will be generous to the bold:
To those who do not fear the dangerous thrust
Of progress toward the far and unforetold,
But know that like a promise freedom must
Lie forward of the darkness, not behind,
And know the Brother in their hearts, and trust
This Light at last to liberate mankind.
If everywhere we search immensity
We know that God is in us, and is true,
However dimly: then we shall be free.
All this expanse of energy and plan—
Stretch out before us, like the old frontiers,
To use and master in the name of man.
Freedom must generate in progress—this
Is what it means to be American.
The vision that the world is waiting is
The same that traced its way in wagon-tracks
Across empurpled plain and precipice,
And whispered in the starlit tamaracks
Where travelers told of freedom in the West
Around the fires of hopeful bivouacs:
The vision of a mighty purpose, pressed
By all the peoples of the earth, to make
The hidden truth within them manifest:
And as this continent was free to take,
And thus awoke the hope of all mankind,
So now, in hope, we hear the future break
On the unsovereigned beaches of the mind.
From science there is liberty to win.
Here is a mighty continent, to face,
To open, to develop, and to free.

This is the land of those who utilize
The love that acts within them like the pull
Of star to star, planet to satellite;
The love of man to man, the powerful,
The mystic source of freedom's every right,
Which signals across bloody battlefields
For us the weary peoples to unite.
It is no easy shore. Adventure yields
To mockery, which arms the prejudiced;
To wealth and all the power that it wields;
To cynic, misanthrope, and atheist:
They will not know the truth who cannot bear
The pain of love, nor will their deeds persist,
Nor will their standard, lifted anywhere,
Protect the earth from bloody dreams of hate:
But only those with courage to prepare
The chamber of the heart will celebrate
The wedding-day of truth and liberty.
This is the needle's eye, the narrow gate,
That leads beyond the horizons that we see,
To what has never been, but yet will be.
America lives in her simple homes:
The weathered door, the old wisteria vine,
The dusty barnyard where the rooster roams,
The common trees like elm and oak and pine:
In furniture for comfort, not for looks,
In names like Jack and Pete and Caroline,
In neighbors you can trust, and honest books,
And peace, and hope, and opportunity.
She lives like destiny in Mom, who cooks
On gleaming stoves her special fricassee,
And jams and cakes and endless apple pies.
She lives in Pop, the family referee,
Absorbing Sunday news with heavy eyes;

And in the dog, and in the shouting kids
Returning home from school, to memorize
The history of the ancient pyramids.
And still she lives in them when darkness wakes
The distant smells and infinite katydids,
And valleys seem like black and fearsome lakes
Guarded by windows of American light,
While in the wind the family maple rakes
The lucent stars westward across the night;
And still, however far her sons may go,
To venture or to die beyond her sight,
These little windows shine incognito
Across incredulous humanity;
That all the peoples of the earth may know
The embattled destination of the free—
Not peace, not rest, not pleasure—but to dare
To face the axiom of democracy;
Freedom is not to limit, but to share;
And freedom here is freedom everywhere.

—*Russell W. Davenport,* MY COUNTRY

The Liberty Song*

Come join hand in hand, brave Americans all,
And rouse your bold hearts at fair Liberty's call;
No tyrannous acts shall suppress your just claim
Or stain with dishonor America's name.

* THE MUSIC FOR THIS SONG IS TO BE FOUND IN *A Treasury
of American Song* (SECOND EDITION, PAGE 56), EDITED BY
ELIE SIEGMEISTER AND OLIN DOWNES, PUBLISHED BY ALFRED
A. KNOPF, INC., NEW YORK.

CHORUS
In freedom we're born and in freedom we'll live.
Our purses are ready. Steady, friends, steady.
Not as slaves, but as free men our money we'll give.

Our worthy forefathers—let's give them a cheer—
To climates unknown and courageously steer;
Through oceans, to deserts, for freedom they came.
And dying bequeath'd us their freedom and fame.
CHORUS

The tree their own hands had to liberty rear'd;
They liv'd to behold growing strong and rever'd;
With transport they cry'd, "Now our witness we gain,
For our children shall gather the fruits of our pain."
CHORUS

Swarms of placemen and pensioners soon will appear
Like locusts deforming the charms of the year;
Suns vainly will rise, showers vainly descend,
If we are to drudge for what others shall spend.
CHORUS

Then join hand in hand, brave Americans all,
By uniting we stand, by dividing we fall;
In so righteous a cause let us hope to succeed
For heaven approves of each generous deed.
CHORUS

All ages shall speak with amaze and applause,
Of the courage we'll show in support of our laws;
To die we can bear—but to serve we disdain,
For shame is to freedom more dreadful than pain.
CHORUS

—John Dickinson

63

Meditation on American Freedom

OUR CONSTITUTION and our history speak of liberty and of the struggles and sacrifices by which liberty was won. To all the world they proclaim the glory of a nation created not to make its leaders strong but to make its people free. And to all Americans they hold a message vital in its import, compelling in its urgency. Freedom is never permanently secure. By each successive generation it must be defended anew. Always its price remains eternal vigilance. Always its preservation demands faith and valor and sacrifice. And freedom is a peculiar trust of our nation. Here, free government was established; here it must be preserved. With the privileges that liberty brings comes the responsibility of upholding it. But, runs a solemn assurance, in our battle to keep men free, we do not fight alone. Behind each of us is the past free life of America. Back of all of us is the spirit of the Founders, which our national shrines immortalize. Washington is with us, and Jefferson and Lincoln. . . . All who fought for freedom, all who knew the great devotion, are still our comrades and exemplars. With such a comradeship, we cannot hesitate. With such a leadership, we cannot fail. Under such a responsibility we dare not falter. We must hold high the light of liberty. That is America's message to all her citizens. That is her message to us—

> "For what avail the plow or sail,
> Or land, or life, if freedom fail."

—*Raymond Pitcairn*, IF FREEDOM FAIL

The Spiritual Heritage of America

WE THANK THEE, O Lord, for having imbued the Founding Fathers of our nation with that faith in Thee which moved them to proclaim truths of great moral import:

> That all men are created equal, that they are endowed by their Creator with certain inalienable rights, that among these are life, liberty, and the pursuit of happiness.

Thou didst guide them in the framing of a constitution designed to promote the general welfare and to secure the blessings of liberty to themselves and their posterity.

> They made provision that all men should be free to serve Thee as their own conscience dictates.

They sought to keep far from these shores the old-world prejudices and fanatical hatreds by which men have profaned Thy name.

> America was to be a nation that, in the words of Washington, "gives to bigotry no sanction, to persecution no assistance."

We thank Thee, O God, for having taught the founders of our Republic laws that safeguard the equal rights of all citizens and impose equal obligations upon all.

> Thus is the happiness of every American bound up with the welfare of the nation by a solemn covenant of citizenship.

Yet not always and not in all ways have we been true to the high purposes of the Founding Fathers; but when we went astray, Thou didst summon us back to the path of righteousness.

> Thou didst send us leaders of prophetic stamp who recalled us to our duty, and who taught us to behold Thy chastening hand in the sufferings and trials brought on by our sins.

O God, help us to keep America true to its faith in democracy and to fulfill the promise of its nationhood.

> Unite the hearts of all Americans, whatever be their race, religion, or part in the nation's economy, and help them preserve and enrich the American heritage of liberty and justice, of democracy and brotherhood.

Protect us from all enemies who, knowing not Thy way of justice and freedom, would seek to destroy or enslave us.

> And protect us also from our own inclination to seek personal, partisan, racial, or sectarian aggrandizement.

Give us love and understanding; may we recognize one another's needs, and help one another in achieving all the worthy purposes we cherish for ourselves and for our people.

> Help us to respect and value the heritage of every community in our land, and enable each community to give of its best to the service of all.

May our nation be privileged to prove, both in its own life and in its dealing with other nations, how good and how beautiful it is for brethren to dwell together in unity.

—*Jewish Reconstructionist Foundation, Inc.*
SABBATH PRAYER BOOK

To Him from Whom Our Blessings Flow *

To Him from Whom our blessings flow,
Who all our wants supplies,
This day the choral song and vow
From grateful hearts shall rise.

'Twas He who led the pilgrim band
Across the stormy sea;
'Twas He who stayed the tyrant's hand
And set our country free.

Be Thou our nation's strength and shield
In manhood and in youth;
Thine arm for our protection wield,
And guide us by Thy truth.

—*Anonymous*

* THE MUSIC FOR THIS SONG IS TO BE FOUND IN *Hymns for the Living Age* (PAGE 228), EDITED BY H. AUGUSTINE SMITH, PUBLISHED BY THE FLEMING H. REVELL COMPANY, NEW YORK.

Closing Prayer

OUR GOD and God of our fathers, Thou presidest over the destinies of men and nations. All of them owe allegiance to Thy law of universal justice and right. The peace and welfare of all depend on their acceptance of Thy law as supreme. Grant that our nation may ever acknowledge Thy sway. May we never in the pride of our power be moved to seek domination over other peoples. May we never, in our enjoyment of ease and luxury, turn a deaf ear to the cry of the oppressed and impoverished of other lands. May we ever extend to other nations the hand of friendship, and strive for the unity of all mankind, that together we may effect the abolition of oppression, poverty, disease and war. Speed Thou the day when those blessings which Thou hast showered on our country may become the common heritage of all men and nations. AMEN.

ARBOR

DAY

A Day Devoted to the Responsible Use of Our Natural Resources

A Note on the Observation of Arbor Day

Arbor Day was designed to ensure the replenishment of the arboreal resources that have been destroyed. Its central feature should be the planting of trees. That practical purpose should be given a religious significance which the following program endeavors to interpret.

The Significance of the Day

WE ARE ASSEMBLED today under God's heaven to express the gratitude that is in our hearts for the trees of forest and orchard, for all growth of the soil, and for all the living creatures that, like us, can find shelter and sustenance in the products of wood and field. We acknowledge our dependence on them and our responsibility to their Creator. May we ever use the gifts they offer us for the good of all men. May we never waste this store of blessing. May we never rob the generations to come of their heritage. Let us instead, by our planting, replenish the wealth of vegetation which we consume for our needs.

We thank Thee, O God, not only for the uses of trees, but also for their beauty. That beauty helps sustain the spirit of man, calming him in his anxieties, cheering him in his disappointments, and comforting him in his sorrows. It is a token of divine love, an assurance of the goodness of life, of man's at-homeness in the universe, as in the house of a loving Father.

We acknowledge on this day our *kinship* with the trees of the forest. Like them we are born, we grow, we die. Like them, our lives are rooted in the soil of our country. As they grow by the light of day, so does our civilization thrive by the spiritual light of truth. And even as the trees perish, but the forest survives, so do we perish but the nation endures. And even as the dead leaves and the roots of dead trees fertilize the soil, and give nourishment to fresh growth, so do the deeds of departed generations nourish the growth of the generations yet unborn.

We therefore invoke Thy blessing, O God, upon all growing things, upon America and the civilization that is the growth of its soil. Cause the cleansing water of Thy grace to rain upon it and the radiant sunshine of Thy love to shine upon it that our nation may live forever and give to all who partake in its life a share in its immortality. AMEN.

The Spacious Firmament on High*

The spacious firmament on high,
With all the blue ethereal sky,
And spangled heav'ns, a shining frame,
Their great Original proclaim.
The unwearied sun, from day to day,
Does his Creator's power display,
And publishes to ev'ry land
The work of an Almighty hand.

Soon as the evening shades prevail,
The moon takes up the wondrous tale,
And nightly to the lis'ning earth
Repeats the story of her birth;
Whilst all the stars that round her burn,
And all the planets in their turn,
Confirm the tidings as they roll
And spread the truth from pole to pole.

What though, in solemn silence, all
Move round the dark terrestrial ball?
What though no real voice nor sound
Amidst their radiant orbs be found?
In reason's ear they all rejoice,
And utter forth a glorious voice,
Forever singing as they shine,
"The hand that made us is divine."

—*Joseph Addison*

*THE MUSIC FOR THIS POEM IS TO BE FOUND IN *Assembly Songs and Choruses* (PAGE 219), EDITED BY RANDALL J. CONDON, HELEN S. LEAVITT, AND ELBRIDGE W. NEWTON, PUBLISHED BY GINN AND COMPANY, BOSTON.

Our Dependence on Nature

SIX AMERICANS out of ten live in cities. They turn a faucet . . . and expect water. Adjust their heat with a flick of the finger. The mere raising of a phone produces their food. Wonderful? Sure! But . . .

Man, with all his scientific knowledge, cannot create an egg, an orange . . . a quart of milk.

He can increase production, overcome the vast difficulties of distribution. He can alter his environment—for better or worse. He can write disturbing words on paper. But he still can't create the tree that is the source of paper.

America has plenty of clothes—food—and the many varieties of material goods that make life pleasant. But their *source* is nature. And with all our science we are still dependent on nature and our knowledge of it.

—*Maxwell S. Stewart*

Our Sacrilegious Treatment of Trees

WE HAVE SINNED against the trees and in our abuse of them have sinned against our country and our God. For centuries now the matchless forests of this country have been disturbed with the cry of "Kill! Kill!" There has been no mercy and no recourse. Slaughter has been waged unhindered and unrebuked. The waste has been more than the product.

> For bark, for charcoal and firewood, for fence-posts and railroad ties, for lumber and shingles, for spars and ship-timbers, for woodenware, matches, and even tooth-picks—for these we have destroyed our forests.

Let us set up laws for the saving of our forests, laws sharp and usable as axes.

> Let our laws proclaim that the ownership of woodland does not carry the right to abuse it,

that private greed may not despoil the public of wealth with which God has endowed our land.

There is a sanctity in natural growth which goes up to the sublimity of the great mountains. To violate this is to degrade ourselves.

This world is something more than a work-shop, and a sin against the sanctity of any created thing is a sin against our own souls.

How many of us have ever really seen a tree? We focus our eyes on so many things which in reality we never see at all. Let us not be blind to the common things around us. For the common things are often the most wonderful.

Let us not be blind to trees.

Behold one of the thousands and millions of leaves on a tree! What is a leaf? How little we can learn about it from dictionary definitions or from what our senses can report to us. All the rest is a divine mystery.

Whoever could tell us just what a leaf is and by what strange action of air and sunlight and earth it comes to be a leaf—his would transcend the wisdom of the ages.

Trees are common. Yes, but what a time it took Mother Nature, working incessantly, to evolve out of the low one-celled plant with which vegetation on earth began, the beautiful, noble monarch of the plant kingdom which we call a tree?

"The groves were God's first temples."

Truly, each tree is a temple. Its living columns are overlaid with the ruby and topaz of summer sunlight and with the pearl and diamond dust of winter.

It is a shrine where the spirit of man may look up. It is a monument to what has been, a heavenward pointing testimony to the Power that lies at the heart of things.

—*Adapted from an anonymous essay,*
CRIMINAL TREATMENT OF TREES,
and from Anna Bagastad, A TEMPLE

The Brooklet *

On the hill there stands an oak tree,
On the hill there stands an oak tree,
And nearby a white birch is growing,
And nearby a white birch is growing.

And between the birch and oak tree,
And between the birch and oak tree,
Runs a little brooklet flowing,
Runs a little brooklet flowing.

On through woods and on through meadows,
On through woods and on through meadows,
Leaps 'neath sun and soft breezes blowing,
Leaps 'neath sun and soft breezes blowing.

Quickly speed thee to the river,
Quickly speed thee to the river,
None can stay thy restless going,
None can stay thy restless going.

—Anonymous

* THE MUSIC FOR THIS SONG IS TO BE FOUND IN *The Ditty
Bag,* EDITED AND PUBLISHED BY JANET E. TOBITT, 416 WEST
33RD STREET, NEW YORK.

Forest Hymn

The groves were God's first temples. Ere man learned
To hew the shaft and lay the architrave,
And spread the roof above them—ere he framed
The lofty vault to gather and roll back
The sound of anthems—in the darkling wood,
Amidst the cool and silence, he knelt down
And offered to the Mightiest solemn thanks
And supplications.

     For his simple heart
Might not resist the sacred influences
That from the stilly twilight of the place,
And from the gray old trunks that high in heaven
Mingled their mossy boughs, and from the sound
Of the invisible breath that swayed at once
All their green tops, stole over him, and bowed
His spirit with the thought of boundless Power
And inaccessible Majesty.

77

        Ah! Why
Should we, in the world's riper years, neglect
God's ancient sanctuaries, and adore
Only among the crowd, and under roofs
That our frail hands have raised?

        Father, Thy hand
Hath reared these venerable columns. Thou
Didst weave this verdant roof. Thou didst look down
Upon the naked earth, and forthwith rose
All these fair ranks of trees . . .
My heart is awed within me when I think
Of the great miracle that still goes on
In silence round me—the perpetual work
Of Thy creation, finished, yet renewed
Forever. Written on Thy works I read
The lesson of Thy own eternity.
Lo! All grow old and die; but see again
How, on the faltering footsteps of decay,
Youth presses—ever gay and beautiful youth—
In all its beautiful forms. These lofty trees
Wave not less proudly than their ancestors
Molder beneath them.

        Oh, there is not lost
One of earth's charms: upon her bosom yet.
After the flight of untold centuries,
The freshness of her fair beginning dies,
And yet shall be. Life mocks the idle hate
Of his arch-enemy Death; yet, seats himself
Upon the sepulchre, and blossoms and smiles,
And of the triumphs of his ghastly foe
Makes his own nourishment. For he came forth
From thine own bosom, and shall have no end.

                            —*William Cullen Bryant*

The Conservation of Natural Resources

The duty of conserving our forest wealth and all our natural resources is one that should be formulated in terms of law. A conference of governors called to consider this problem met at the White House and, on May 13, 1908, adopted a declaration of principles, including the following statement.

WE, the governors of the states and territories of the United States of America in conference assembled, do hereby declare the conviction that the great prosperity of our country rests upon the abundant resources of the land. . . .

We look upon these resources as a heritage to be made use of in establishing and promoting the comfort, prosperity, and happiness of the American people, but not to be wasted, deteriorated, or needlessly destroyed.

We agree that land should be so used that erosion and soil wash shall cease, and that there should be reclamation of arid and semi-arid regions by means of irrigation, and of swamp and overflowed regions by means of drainage; that the waters should be so preserved and used as to promote navigation, to enable this arid region to be reclaimed by irrigation, and to develop power in the interest of the people; that the forests which regulate our rivers, support our industries, and promote the fertility and productiveness of the soil should be preserved and perpetuated; that the minerals found so abundantly beneath the surface should be so used as to prolong their utility; that the beauty, healthfulness, and habitability of our country should be preserved and increased; that sources of national wealth exist for the benefit of the people, and that monopoly thereof should not be tolerated.

Johnny Appleseed *

Johnny Appleseed!
Johnny Appleseed!

Of Jonathan Chapman two things are known:
That he loved apples, that he walked alone.
At seventy odd he was gnarled as could be,
But ruddy and sound as a good apple tree.
For fifty years over of harvest and dew,
He planted his apples where no apples grew.
The winds of the prairie might blow through his rags,
But he carried his seed in deer skin bags.

Johnny Appleseed! Johnny Appleseed! Johnny Apple-
     seed!

From Ashtabula to Fort Wayne,
He planted and pruned, and planted again.
He had no hat to encumber his head,
But wore a tin pan on his white hair instead.
A fine old man as ripe as a pippin,
His heart still light and his step still skipping.
He nested with owl, with bear cub and possum,
And knew all his orchards, root, tendril and blossom.

80

Johnny Appleseed! Johnny Appleseed! Johnny Appleseed!

The stalking Indian, the beast in its lair,
Did no hurt while he was there,
For they could tell, as wild things can,
That Jonathan Chapman was God's own man.
Why did he do it? We do not know
He wished that apples might root and grow.
He has no statue, he has no tomb,
But he has his apple trees still in bloom.
Johnny Appleseed! Johnny Appleseed! Johnny Apple-
seed!

—*Rosemary Benét*

*THE MUSIC FOR THIS SONG IS TO BE FOUND IN *A Treasury
of American Song* (SECOND EDITION, PAGE 314), EDITED BY
OLIN DOWNES AND ELIE SIEGMEISTER, PUBLISHED BY ALFRED A.
KNOPF, INC., NEW YORK.

Trees

I think that I shall never see
A poem lovely as a tree.
A tree whose hungry mouth is prest
Against the earth's sweet flowing breast.
A tree that looks at God all day
And lifts her leafy arms to pray.
A tree that may in summer wear
A nest of robins in her hair.
Upon whose bosom snow has lain;
Who intimately lives with rain.

Poems are made by fools like me,
But only God can make a tree.

—Joyce Kilmer

Our Duty to the Soil

OUR MODERN INSTITUTION—Arbor Day—
is a public acknowledgement of our dependence upon
the soil of the earth for our daily, our annual, bread.
In recognition of the same fact the Emperor of China
annually plowed a furrow with his own hand, and in
the same significance are the provisions in the ancient
law of Moses, to give the land its seven-year Sabbath,
as well as to man his seventh day for rest and recreation. Our observance is a better one, because it calls on
all, and especially on the impressible learners in the
schools, to join in the duty which we owe to the earth
and to all mankind of doing what each of us can to
preserve the soil's fertility, and to prevent, as long as
possible, the earth, from which we have our being,
from becoming worn out and wholly bald and bare.
And we do this by planting of any sort, if only by
making two blades of grass grow where but one grew
before, and by learning to preserve vegetation. We
give solemnity to this observance by joining in it on
an appointed day, high and low, old and young together.

—Anonymous

AT THIS POINT IN THE PROGRAM, A TREE IS PLANTED

A Hymn for Arbor Day*

God save this tree we plant!
And to all nature grant
    Sunshine and rain.
Let not its branches fade,
Save it from axe and spade,
Save it for joyful shade—
    Guarding the plane.

When it is ripe to fall
Neighbored by trees as tall
    Shape it for good.
Shape it to bench and stool
Shape it to square and rule,
Shape it for home and school,
    God bless the wood.

Lord of the earth and sea,
Prosper our planted tree,
    Save with Thy might.
Save us from indolence,
Waste and improvidence,
And in Thy excellence
    Lead us aright.

—*Henry Hamby Hay*

* TO BE SUNG TO THE TUNE OF "AMERICA."

God of the Open Air

While the tremulous leafy haze on the woodland is
    spreading,
And the bloom on the meadow betrays where May
    has been treading,
While the birds in the branches above, and the brooks
    flowing under,
Are singing together of love in a world full of wonder,
(Lo! In the marvel of Springtime, dreams are changed
    into truth!)
Quicken my heart, and restore the beautiful hopes of
    youth.

By the faith which the flowers show when they bloom
    unbidden,
By the calm of a river's flow to a goal that is hidden,
By the trust of the tree that clings to its deep founda-
    tion,
By the courage of wild birds' wings on the long migra-
    tion,
(Wonderful secret of peace that abides in Nature's
    breast!)
Teach me how to confide, and live my life, and rest.

—*Henry Van Dyke*

Through All the World*

Through all the world below,
God is seen all around;

84

Search hills and valleys through,
There he's found.
The growing of the corn,
The lily and the thorn,
The pleasant and forlorn,
All declare God is there,
In the meadows dressed in green,
There he's seen.

See springs of water rise,
Fountains flow, rivers run;
The mist below the skies
Hides the sun;
Then down the rain doth pour,
The ocean it doth roar,
And dash against the shore,
All to praise, in their lays,
That God that ne'er declines
His designs.

The sun, to my surprise,
Speaks of God as he flies;
The comets in their blaze
Give him praise;
The shining of the stars
The moon as it appears
His sacred name declares;
See them shine, all divine!
The shades in silence prove
God's above.

—Anonymous

* THE MUSIC FOR THIS SONG IS TO BE FOUND IN *A Treasury of American Song* (SECOND EDITION, PAGE 126), EDITED BY OLIN DOWNES AND ELIE SIEGMEISTER, PUBLISHED BY ALFRED A. KNOPF, INC., NEW YORK.

Closing Prayer

O GOD, Creator of all that lives, we have planted a tree in token of our acknowledgement of the duty that rests upon us to further Thy work of creation. It is upon Thee, however, and upon Thy gifts of rain and sunshine and nourishing soil that the growth of this tree depends.

And so is it with all our works in making this a better world. Every good deed we do is but a seed, taken from the store of Thine infinite goodness, planted by us in this world and dependent upon Thy creative and sustaining power to enable it to thrive and bear fruit.

Our fathers planted a good seed, the seed of a self-governing society of free and equal citizens. Instruct us in Thy law so that we may know how to prune the tree which they planted of all unwholesome growths, and how so to cultivate it with loving and patient labor that today's new shoots may ever draw the sap of life from the deepest roots of our American past. May our nation be indeed a tree of life bearing blossoms of beauty and fruit of goodness for endless ages. AMEN.

MAY 30

MEMORIAL

DAY

A Day Devoted to Reflection
on Sacrifice for American Ideals

The Significance of the Day

ON THIS DAY, we call to mind those who gave their lives that our nation might live. Alas that its preservation should have entailed the loss of so much treasure, should have brought so much suffering, should have demanded so many young and promising lives! The only fitting memorial to those sacrifices is our self-dedication to the task of abolishing all inner strife, hatred, and bitterness from among us.

May the remembrance of the price we paid for our life as a nation impel us to seek justice, to foster freedom, and to pursue the ways of peace. May our nation be a source of blessing to all its people and to the rest of mankind.

Responsive Reading

Let us bear in mind on this day of Memorial, that the only object of arms is to bring about a condition in which quiet peace under liberty can endure.

A peace which shall cause men at length to lay down weapons of hatred and to forego unrighteous ambitions which create fear.

Let us seek a language in which neighbor can talk to neighbor, and by which the common and homely and human instincts found everywhere may reach expression through elimination of fear.

Let us try, in all simplicity, to find the road toward this peace. Let the goal of our dearest desire be a quiet peace under liberty.

—*Adapted from* FRANKLIN D. ROOSEVELT

Tenting Tonight

We're tenting tonight on the old camp ground;
Give us a song to cheer
Our weary hearts, a song of home
And friends we love so dear.

CHORUS
Many are the hearts that are weary tonight,
Wishing for the war to cease;
Many are the hearts that are looking for the right,
To see the dawn of peace.
Tenting tonight, tenting tonight,
Tenting on the old camp ground.

We've been tenting tonight on the old camp ground,
Thinking of days gone by,
Of the loved ones at home that gave us the hand,
And the tear that said "good-bye."
CHORUS

We're tired of war on the old camp ground;
Many are dead and gone,
Of the brave and true who've left their homes,
Others been wounded long.
CHORUS

—Walter Kittredge

The Battle-field

Once this soft turf, this rivulet's sands,
　　Were trampled by a hurrying crowd,
And fiery hearts and armed hands
　　Encountered in the battle-cloud.

Ah! never shall the land forget
　　How gushed the life-blood of her brave—
Gushed, warm with hope and courage yet,
　　Upon the soil they fought to save.

Now all is calm, and fresh, and still;
　　Alone the chirp of flitting bird,
And talk of children on the hill,
　　And bell of wandering kine, are heard.

No solemn host goes trailing by
　　The black-mouthed gun and staggering wain;
Men start not at the battle-cry,
　　Oh, be it never heard again!

Soon rested those who fought; but thou
　　Who minglest in the harder strife
For truths which men receive not now,
　　Thy warfare only ends with life.

A friendless warfare! lingering long
　　Through weary day and weary year;
A wild and many-weaponed throng
　　Hang on thy front, and flank, and rear.

Yet nerve thy spirit to the proof,
　　And blench not at thy chosen lot,
The timid good may stand aloof,
　　The sage may frown—yet faint thou not.

Nor heed the shaft too surely cast,
　　The foul and hissing bolt of scorn;
For with thy side shall swell, at last,
　　The victory of endurance born.

Truth, crushed to earth, shall rise again;
　　Th' eternal years of God are hers;
But Error, wounded, writhes in pain,
　　And dies among his worshipers.

Yea, though thou lie upon the dust,
　　When they who helped thee flee in fear,
Die full of hope and manly trust,
　　Like those who fell in battle here.

Another hand thy sword shall wield,
　　Another hand the standard wave,
Till from the trumpet's mouth is pealed
　　The blast of triumph o'er thy grave.

　　　　　　　　　　—William Cullen Bryant

That America's Heroes Shall Not Have Died in Vain

MEMORIAL DAY is a day of solemn memories and inspiring reflections.

　　It reminds us of the lives that were sacrificed in the struggle to save the nation.

How can we redeem the waste of human life, the frustration of the hopes of so many of our youth, the desolated homes and the broken hearts resulting from the wars in which our nation engaged?

Not by tears and lamentations, and not by erecting monuments in memory of the dead;

Not by boasting of their heroism as though it were our own, and taking glory to ourselves for their sacrifice;

Not by pomp and processions with flaunting banners and flashing weapons, to martial music and the exciting beat of drums.

Only by keeping faith with our heroes can we perpetuate their deeds; only by fulfilling the purposes for which they exposed themselves to death can we redeem their sacrifice from futility.

Grant, O God, that the example of their devotion to their country, which they held dearer than life, may move us to equal loyalty, to a pure and exalted patriotism;

That it impel us to make our country great, its laws just and wise, its culture deep and true, its economy productive, equitable, and free, and its religion profound and pure.

Then will no sacrifice for preserving the nation be too high a price to pay.

If we want indeed to honor the memory of those who gave their lives that the nation might live, let us highly resolve that the dead shall not have died in vain;

That the nation shall, under God, have a new birth of freedom, and that government of the people, for the people, and by the people shall not perish from the earth.

That the world shall be made safe for democracy, and that democracy shall save the world;

That our nation take its place among the family of nations which shall fulfill the ancient prophecy:

"They shall beat their swords into ploughshares and their spears into pruning hooks;

Nation shall not lift up sword against nation, neither shall they learn war any more."

—*Jewish Reconstructionist Foundation, Inc.*
SABBATH PRAYER BOOK

Lincoln's Letter to Mrs. Bixby

For Silent Reading

EXECUTIVE MANSION, WASHINGTON
November 21, 1864
MRS. BIXBY, BOSTON, MASSACHUSETTS.
Dear Madam: I have been shown in the files of the War Department a statement of the Adjutant-General of Massachusetts that you are the mother of five sons

who have died gloriously on the field of battle. I feel how weak and fruitless must be any words of mine which should attempt to beguile you from the grief of a loss so overwhelming. But I cannot refrain from tendering to you the consolation that may be found in the thanks of the Republic they died to save. I pray that our heavenly Father may assuage the anguish of your bereavement, and leave you only the cherished memory of the loved and lost and the solemn pride that must be yours to have laid so costly a sacrifice upon the altar of freedom.

Yours very sincerely and respectfully,

Abraham Lincoln

The Young Dead Soldiers

The young dead soldiers do not speak.
Nevertheless they are heard in the still houses.
(Who has not heard them?)
They have a silence that speaks for them at night
And when the clock counts.
They say,
We were young. We have died. Remember us.
They say,
We have done what we could
But until it is finished it is not done.
They say,
We have given our lives

But until it is finished no one can know what our lives
gave.
They say,
Our deaths are not ours,
They are yours,
They will mean what you make them.
They say,
Whether our lives and our deaths were for peace and
a new hope
Or for nothing
We cannot say.
It is you who must say this.
They say,
We leave you our deaths.
Give them their meaning.
Give them an end to the war and a true peace,
Give them a victory that ends the war and a peace
afterwards,
Give them their meaning.
We were young, they say.
We have died.
Remember us.

—*Archibald MacLeish*

Swing Low Sweet Chariot *

Swing low sweet chariot,
Comin' for to carry me home,
Swing low sweet chariot,
Comin' for to carry me home.
O swing low sweet chariot,
Comin' for to carry me home,
Swing low sweet chariot,
Comin' for to carry me home.

I look'd over Jordan, and what did I see,
Comin' for to carry me home,
A band of angels comin' after me,
Comin' for to carry me home.

If you get-a dere befo' I do,
Comin' for to carry me home,
Tell all my friends I'm comin' too,
Comin' for to carry me home.
O, swing low sweet chariot,
Comin' for to carry me home,
Swing low sweet chariot,
Comin' for to carry me home,
Comin' for to carry me home.

—*Anonymous*

* THE MUSIC FOR THIS SONG IS TO BE FOUND IN *The Books of American Negro Spirituals* (VOLUME I, PAGE 62), EDITED BY J. W. JOHNSON AND J. ROSAMOND JOHNSON, PUBLISHED BY THE VIKING PRESS, NEW YORK.

The Gettysburg Address

Nowhere has the idea that gives meaning to Memorial Day found more eloquent expression than in the address with which President Lincoln dedicated part of the battlefield of Gettysburg as a burial ground for fallen soldiers. Let us read his solemn declaration.

FOURSCORE AND SEVEN YEARS AGO our fathers brought forth on this continent a new nation, conceived in liberty, and dedicated to the proposition that all men are created equal.

Now we are engaged in a great civil war, testing whether that nation, or any nation so conceived and so dedicated, can long endure. We are met on a great battlefield of that war. We have come to dedicate a portion of that field as a final resting-place for those who here gave their lives that that nation might live. It is altogether fitting and proper that we should do this.

But, in a larger sense, we cannot dedicate—we cannot consecrate—we cannot hallow—this ground. The brave men, living and dead, who struggled here, have consecrated it far above our poor power to add or detract. The world will little note nor long remember what we say here, but it can never forget what they did here. It is for us, the living, rather, to be dedicated here to the unfinished work which they who fought here have thus far so nobly advanced. It is rather for us to be here dedicated to the great task remaining before us—that from these honored dead we take increased devotion to that cause for which they gave the last full measure of devotion; that we here highly resolve that these dead shall not have died in vain; that this nation, under God, shall have a new birth of freedom; and that government of the people, by the people, for the people, shall not perish from the earth.

A Tribute to Those Who Fell at Iwo Jima

We cannot read the tribute of Abraham Lincoln to the fallen heroes of the Civil War without being reminded also of those who fell in defense of our nation and of its democratic way of life in more recent wars. The following tribute by an American chaplain to the dead who were buried on Iwo Jima will help us to realize the debt we owe them.

THIS IS PERHAPS THE GRIMMEST, and surely the holiest, task we have faced since D-Day. Before us lie the bodies of comrades and friends, men who until yesterday or last week laughed with us, joked with us, trained with us, men who were on the same ships with us, and went over the sides with us as we prepared to hit the beaches on this island, men who fought with us and feared with us.

Somewhere in this plot of ground there may lie the man who could have discovered the cure for cancer. Under one of these Christian crosses, or beneath a Jewish Star of David, there may rest now a man who was destined to be a great prophet . . . to find the way, perhaps, for all to live in plenty. . . . Now they lie here silently in this sacred soil, and we gather to consecrate this earth in their memory.

. . . To speak in memory of such men as these is not easy. Of them, too, can it be said with utter truth: "The world will little note nor long remember what we say here. It can never forget what they did here."

. . . These men have done their job well. They have paid the ghastly price of freedom. If that freedom be once again lost, as it was after the last war, the unforgivable blame will be ours, not theirs. So it is we "the living" who are here to be dedicated and consecrated.

We dedicate ourselves, first, to live together in peace the way they fought and are buried in this war. Here lie men who loved America because their ancestors generations ago helped in her founding, and other men who loved her with equal passion, because they themselves or their own fathers escaped from oppression to her blessed shores. Here lie officers and men, Negroes and Whites, rich men and poor . . . together. Here are Protestants, Catholics, and Jews . . . together. Here no man prefers another because of his faith or despises him because of his color. . . .

Any man among us, "the living," who fails to understand that will thereby betray those who lie here dead. . . . To this, then, as our solemn, sacred duty, do we the living now dedicate ourselves: to the right of Protestants, Catholics, and Jews, of White men and Negroes alike, to enjoy the democracy for which all of them have here paid the price.

To one thing more do we consecrate ourselves in memory of those who sleep beneath these crosses and stars. . . . This war, with all its frightful heartache and suffering, is but the beginning of our generation's struggle for democracy. When the last battle has been won, there will be those at home, as there were last time, who will want us to turn our backs in selfish isolation on the rest of organized humanity, and thus to sabotage the very peace for which we fight. We promise you who lie here: we will not do that! . . .

When the last shot has been fired, there will still be those whose eyes are turned backward, not forward, who will be satisfied with those wide extremes of poverty and wealth in which the seeds of another war can be sown. We promise you, our departed comrades: this, too, we will not permit. This war has been fought by the common man! We promise, by all that is sacred and holy, that your sons—the sons of miners and millers, the sons of farmers and workers—will inherit from your death the right to a living that is decent and secure.

When the final cross has been placed in the last cemetery, once again there will be those to whom profit is more important than peace, who will insist with the voice of sweet reasonableness and appeasement that it is better to trade with the enemies of mankind than, by crushing them, to lose their profit. To you who sleep here silently, we give our promise: we will not listen! We will not forget that some of you were burnt with oil that came from American wells, that many of you were killed by shells fashioned from American steel. We promise that when once again men seek profit at your expense, we shall remember how you looked when we placed you reverently, lovingly, in the ground.

Thus do we memorialize those who, having ceased living with us, now live within us. Thus do we consecrate ourselves, the living, to carry on the struggle they began. Too much blood has gone into this soil for us to let it lie barren. Too much pain and heartache have fertilized the earth on which we stand. We here solemnly swear: this shall not be in vain! Out of this, and from the suffering and sorrow of those who mourn, this will come—we promise—the birth of a new freedom for the sons of men everywhere. AMEN.

—Roland B. Gittelsohn

The Whole Wide World Around*

Because all men are brothers,
Wherever men may be,
No fascist shall defeat us,
No nation strike us down.
All men who toil shall greet us
The whole wide world around.

One union shall unite us,
Forever proud and free.
No fascist shall defeat us,
No nation strike us down.
All men who toil shall greet us
The whole wide world around.

My brothers are all others,
Forever hand in hand;
Wherever people struggle,
There is my native land.

* THE MUSIC FOR THIS SONG IS TO BE FOUND IN *The People's Song Book* (PAGE 96), EDITED BY WALDEMAR HILLE, PUBLISHED BY BONI & GAER, INC., NEW YORK.

My brother's fears are my fears—
Yellow, White and Brown;
My brother's tears are my tears,
The whole wide world around.

Let every voice be thunder,
Let every heart be stone,
Until all tyrants perish
Our work shall not be done.
Let every pain be token,
The lost years shall be found.
Let slavery's chain be broken
The whole wide world around.

—*Tom Glazer*

Prayer for Peace

Lord God of trajectory and blast
Whose terrible sword has laid open the serpent
So it withers in the sun for the just to see,
Sheathe now the swift avenging blade with the names
      of nations writ on it,

And assist in the preparation of the ploughshare.

Lord God of fresh bread and tranquil mornings,
Who walks in the circuit of heaven among the worthy,
Deliver notice to the fallen young men
That tokens of orange juice and a whole egg appear
      now before the hungry children;

    That night again falls cooling on the earth as
      quietly as when it leaves your hand;

    That Freedom has withstood the tyrant like a Malta
      in a hostile sea,

    And that the soul of man is surely a Sevastopol
      which goes down hard and leaps from ruin
      quickly.

Lord God of the topcoat and the living wage
Who has furred the fox against the time of winter
And stored provender of bees in summer's brightest
      places,
Do bring sweet influence to bear upon the assembly
      line:

    Accept the smoke of the milltown among the
      accredited clouds of the sky:

Fend from the wind with a house and a hedge, him
      whom you made in your image:
And permit him to pick of the tree and the flock,

    That he may eat today without fear of tomorrow
    And clothe himself with dignity in December.

Lord God of test-tube and blueprint
Who jointed molecules of dust and shook them till
      their name was Adam,

Who taught worms and stars how they could live together,

Appear now among the parliaments of nations
and give instruction to their schemes.

Measure out new liberties so none shall suffer for his
father's color or the credo of his choice.

Post proofs that brotherhood is not so wild a
dream as those who profit by postponing it
pretend.

Sit at the treaty table and convoy the hopes of little
peoples through expected straits,
And press into the final seal a sign that peace will come
for longer than posterities can see ahead,

That man unto his fellow man shall be a friend
forever. AMEN.

—Adapted from Norman Corwin,
ON A NOTE OF TRIUMPH

Who Are the People?

The people is Everyman, everybody.
Everybody is you and me and all others.
What everybody says is what we all say.
And what is it we all say?

Where did we get these languages?
When shall we all speak the same language?
And do we want to have all the same language?
Are we learning a few great signs and passwords?
Why should Everyman be lost for words?
The questions are put every day in every tongue:
"Where are you from, Stranger?
Where were you born?
Got any money?
What do you work at?
Where's your passport?
Who are your people?"

Over the ether crash the languages.
And the people listen.

They will be told when the next war is ready.
The long wars and the short wars will come on the air,
How many got killed and how the war ended
And who got what and the price paid
And how there were tombs for the Unknown Soldier,
The boy nobody knows the name of,
The boy whose great fame is that of the masses,
The millions of names too many to write on a tomb,
The heroes, the cannonfodder, the living targets,
The mutilated and sacred dead,
The people, yes.

Two countries with two flags
Are nevertheless one land, one blood, one people—
can this be so?
And the earth belongs to the family of man?
can this be so?

The first world war came and its cost was laid on the
        people.
The second world war—the third—what will be the
        cost?
And will it repay the people for what they pay?

        Can the wilderness be put behind?
        Shall man always go on dog-eat-dog?
        Who says so?
        The stronger?
        And who is the stronger?
And how long shall the stronger hold on as the
        stronger?
        What will tomorrow write?
        "Of the people by the people for the people?"
What mockers ever wrung a crop from a waiting soil
Or when did cold logic bring forth a child?
"What use is it?" they asked a kite-flying sky gazer
And he wished in return to know "What use is a
        baby?"
The dreaming scholars who quested the useless,
who wanted to know merely for the sake of knowing,
they sought and harnessed electrodynamic volts
becoming in time thirty billion horses in one country
hauling with thirty-billion-horse-power
and this is an early glimpse, a dim beginning,
the first hill of a series of hills.

Across the bitter years and the howling winters
        the deathless dream will be the stronger
        the dream of equity will win.

        The people will live on
The learning and blundering people will live on.

They will be tricked and sold and again sold
And go back to the nourishing earth for rootholds,
    The people so peculiar in renewal and comeback,
    You can't laugh off their capacity to take it.

    Once having marched
Over the margins of animal necessity,
Over the grim line of sheer subsistence,
    Then man came
To the deeper rituals of his bones,
To the lights lighter than any bones,
To the time for thinking things over,
To the dance, the song, the story,
Or the hours given over to dreaming,
Once having marched.

Between the finite limitations of the five senses
and the endless yearnings of man for the beyond,
people hold to the humdrum bidding of work and food
while reaching out when it comes their way
for lights beyond the prison of the five senses,
for keepsakes lasting beyond any hunger or death.
    This reaching is alive.
The panderers and liars have violated and smutted it,
    Yet this reaching is alive yet
    for lights and keepsakes.

    Man is a long time coming.
Man will yet win.
Brother may yet line up with brother:
This old anvil laughs at many broken hammers.
    There are men who can't be bought.
    The fireborn are at home in fire.
    The stars make no noise.

You can't hinder the wind from blowing.
Time is a great teacher.
Who can live without hope?

In the darkness with a great bundle of grief the people
      march.
In the night, and overhead a shovel of stars for keeps,
      the people march: "Where to? what next?"

—*Carl Sandburg,* THE PEOPLE, YES

Peace Through Cooperation

Peace is good.

Let us by all means make peace between us, and
let us forever keep the peace.

What is good for me is good for you; it is also good
for your children and for my children.

Give me there of your strength tomorrow, and I
will give you here of my strength today.

Neither of us shall be a loser thereby, and each shall
duly profit in the common enterprise.

I will truly tell you of my adventures, of my going out, and my coming in, of my successes, and
of my failures; and you will truly tell me yours.

So shall we multiply our profits, for each shall profit by his own experience and by the experience of his brother.

So shall we both grow in truth, in wisdom, and in our common knowledge.

So may we better act together in our common purposes.

I will keep the faith, even as you will keep the faith, with my life, it may be,

For my goods, my life, and the lives of my helpers, are dependent on the fulfilment of my covenants.

So shall we and our possessions the longer endure.

Our mutual faith, our loyalty, and our honor shall be as a staff to lean upon;

As girders over unmeasured gulfs of time and space;

As invisible bonds binding each to each with hooks of steel, yet leaving each one free.

Our honor shall not stand upon compulsion;

It shall not require a witness, or a guardian, or other pledge than honor;

For the virtue in honor cannot be strengthened save by honor.

So shall our honor be an insurance, valid in full, at whatsoever time or place, against the fickle winds of adversity.

So shall we grow in stability and security.

Our common profits shall be as a reservoir that shall be filled in times of plenty and drawn upon in times of need.

They shall be a heritage to the sons of men, freely given and gladly received, to use and to enjoy.

So shall we grow in benevolence which is our assurance of continued prosperity.

So shall we, and our children, and our children's children, live long in the land and grow in happiness.

Our house of peace shall be built by mutual service.

It shall be founded on truth and sheltered by justice.

So shall fear, and hate, and greed not enter therein.

—*Adapted from William Patten,*
THE GRAND STRATEGY OF EVOLUTION

The Nation *

America, America, The shouts of war shall cease;
The glory dawns! The day is come
Of victory and peace!
And now upon a larger plan
We'll build the common good,
The temple of the love of man
The House of Brotherhood!

What though its stones were laid in tears,
Its pillars red with wrong,
Its walls shall rise through patient years
To soaring spires of song!
For on this house shall faith attend
With joy on airy wing,
And flaming loyalty ascend
To God, the only King!

America, America, Ring out the glad refrain!
Salute the flag—salute the dead
That have not died in vain!
O glory! glory to thy plan
To build the common good,
The temple of the rights of man,
The House of Brotherhood! Amen.

—*Allen Eastman Cross*

* THE MUSIC FOR THIS SONG IS TO BE FOUND IN *Hymns for the Living Age* (PAGE 289), EDITED BY H. AUGUSTINE SMITH, PUBLISHED BY THE FLEMING H. REVELL COMPANY, NEW YORK.

By Our Stairs

When we lie down worn out,
other men will stand young and fresh.
By the steps that we have cut they will climb;
by the stairs that we have built they will mount.
They will never know the names of the men who made
      them.
At the clumsy work they will laugh;
and when the stones roll they will curse us.
But they will mount, and on our work;
they will climb, and by our stairs!
No man liveth to himself,
and no man dieth to himself.

—Olive Schreiner

Closing Prayer

*It is entirely fitting that we conclude this serv-
ice with a declaration of faith, uttered by one of
our fallen heroes, the valiant commander-in-chief
of our armed forces in the late war, President
Franklin Delano Roosevelt.*

WE AFFIRM that life in the centuries that lie ahead
must be based on positive and permanent values.

The value of love will always be stronger than the
value of hate. . . .

The value of a belief in humanity and justice is always stronger in any land than the value of belief in force. . . .

The value of truth and sincerity is always stronger than the value of lies and cynicism. . . . Men cannot be made to believe that a way of life is good when it spreads poverty, misery, disease, and death. Men cannot be everlastingly loyal unless they are free.

We acclaim today the American Way. We are determined to live in peace and to make that peace secure. We are determined to follow the paths of free peoples to a civilization worthy of free men.

—*Franklin D. Roosevelt*

To this solemn affirmation, we pledge ourselves in consecration to the memory of the martyred president who uttered it and of all the heroes and martyrs who gave their lives that our country and its civilization may live. God give us the strength to be steadfast in the fulfillment of this pledge.

FLAG

DAY

A Day Devoted to Reflections on
the Reality Symbolized by the Flag

The Significance of the Day

ON THE FOURTEENTH DAY OF June in the year 1780, the flag of our nation was born. On that day the Congress of the United States resolved "that the flag of the thirteen United States be thirteen stripes, alternate red and white; that the Union be thirteen stars, white in a blue field, representing a new constellation."

Today we celebrate the anniversary of that event. Today, over a vast territory and over the hearts of many millions of people that emblem holds sway, a symbol endowed with immeasurable potency to evoke loyalty, heroism, and self-sacrifice.

We are assembled to renew our allegiance to the flag and to all that it symbolizes. We are not idolaters. Our homage is not to the flag as a piece of colored cloth. It is to what the flag means in our life and the life of mankind; to the land, the persons, the institutions, the laws, the ideals, the human relationships that the flag betokens.

To these our loyalty is directed, and upon these we invoke the blessing of God. Grant, O God, that the display of our national emblem move us so to live that we may never disgrace it, but always reflect honor upon it. May our flag forever remain the symbol of a nation dedicated to freedom, justice, and the well-being of all mankind.

What the Flag Means to Us

WHEN WE SEE THE FLAG OF OUR NATION it is not the flag alone that we see; we see in our mind's eye the nation itself.

> We see the land of the United States stretching from sea to sea, in which our people grappled with nature and wrested from her a divine blessing, becoming the pioneers of the frontier of the world's future.

We see the government of the United States, conceived in liberty and dedicated to the proposition that all men are created equal; a government of universal suffrage based on the will of all the people and protecting the rights of the weak against encroachment by the strong.

> We see the history of the United States; the toil of the colonists to redeem the wilderness for human habitation; the struggle to secure our country's independence and freedom; the agonizing internal struggle to maintain the union and abolish slavery; the efforts to achieve economic freedom for all our people and the battles to make the world safe for democracy and to make democracy a force for world unity.

We see the civilization and culture of the United States, its arts and its sciences, its ways of work and play and worship, the soul of it poured out in song

and story and embodied in folkways and institutions—
all the creation of a free people striving to achieve a
freer and a better life than the world has yet known.

We see in it the hope and faith of our people,
their belief that men are capable of self-government, that, given freedom from fear and want,
they will recognize and submit to Thy law of
truth and right and strive for Thy kingdom of
peace and love.

Grant, O God, that those emotions which the sight of
our flag awakens in our heart may ever find expression
in a loyal devotion to the true interests of our nation,

That, under Thy guidance, our country may grow
from generation to generation in an ever more
abundant and more faithful expression of those
democratic ideals that have led it in all its achievements.

Land That We Love

Land that we love! Thou Future of the World!
Thou refuge of the noble heart oppressed!
Oh never be thy shining image hurled
From its high place in the adoring breast
Of him who worships thee with jealous love!
Keep thou thy starry forehead as the dove
All white, and to the eternal Dawn inclined!
Thou art not for thyself but for mankind,
And to despair of thee were to despair
Of man, of man's high destiny, of God!
Of thee should man despair, the journey trod
Upward, through unknown eons, stair on stair,
By this our race, with bleeding feet and slow,
Were but the pathway to a darker woe
Than yet was visioned by the heavy heart
Of prophet. To despair of thee! Ah no!
For thou thyself art Hope, Hope of the World thou
    art!

> —*Richard Watson Gilder,*
> THE GREAT REMEMBRANCE

Columbia, the Gem of the Ocean

O Columbia! the gem of the ocean,
The home of the brave and the free,
The shrine of each patriot's devotion,
A world offers homage to thee.
Thy mandates make heroes assemble,
When liberty's form stands in view;
Thy banners make tyranny tremble,
When borne by the red, white and blue.

When borne by the red, white and blue,
When borne by the red, white and blue,
Thy banners make tyranny tremble,
When borne by the red, white and blue.

When war wing'd its wide desolation,
And threatened the land to deform,
The ark then of freedom's foundation,
Columbia, rode safe through the storm;
With garlands of vict'ry around her,
When so proudly she bore her brave crew;
With her flag proudly floating before her,
The boast of the red, white and blue.

The boast of the red, white and blue,
The boast of the red, white and blue,
With her flag proudly floating before her,
The boast of the red, white and blue.

—Timothy Dwight

The Land Where Hate Should Die

This is the land where hate should die—
No feuds of faith, no spleen of race,
No darkly brooding fear should try
Beneath our flag to find a place.

Lo! every people here has sent
Its sons to answer freedom's call;
Their lifeblood is the strong cement
That builds and binds the nation's wall.

This is the land where hate should die—
Though dear to me my faith and shrine,
I serve my country well when I
Respect beliefs that are not mine.

He little loves his land who'd cast
Upon his neighbor's word a doubt,
Or cite the wrongs of ages past
From present rights to bar him out.

This is the land where hate should die—
This is the land where strife should cease,
Where foul, suspicious fear should fly
Before our flag of light and peace.

Then let us purge from poisoned thought
That service to the State we give,
And so be worthy as we ought
Of this great land in which we live!

—*Denis A. McCarthy*

Respect for the Flag

So sacred a symbol as the flag of our nation needs to be guarded against sacrilegious use. To enable it to evoke in our hearts the sentiment of a pure and dedicated patriotism, we must invest its use at all times with reverence and associate it with dignity. To that end, certain rules have been formulated by patriotic societies which it is well for all of us to know and to apply.

RULES FOR SHOWING RESPECT FOR THE FLAG

1. Do not permit disrespect to be shown to the flag of the United States of America.

2. Do not dip the flag of the United States of America to any person or any thing.

3. Do not display the flag with the union down except as a signal of distress.

4. Do not place any other flag or pennant above or, if on the same level, to the right of the flag of the United States of America.

5. Do not let the flag touch the ground or the floor or trail in water.

6. Do not place any object or emblem of any kind on or above the flag of the United States of America.

7. Do not use the flag as drapery in any form whatsoever. Use bunting of blue, white and red.

8. Do not fasten the flag in such a manner as will permit it to be easily torn.

9. Do not drape the flag over the hood, top, sides, or back of a vehicle or of a railway train or boat. When the flag is displayed on a motor car, the staff should be affixed firmly to the chassis or clamped to the radiator cap.

10. Do not display the flag on a float in a parade except from a staff.

11. Do not use the flag as a covering for a ceiling.

12. Do not carry the flag flat or horizontally, but always aloft and free.

13. Do not use the flag as a portion of a costume or of an athletic uniform. Do not embroider it upon cushions or handkerchiefs or print it on paper napkins and boxes.

14. Do not put lettering of any kind upon the flag.

15. Do not use the flag in any form of advertising or fasten an advertising sign to a pole from which the flag is flown.

16. Do not display, use, or store the flag in such a manner as will permit it to be easily soiled or damaged.

—State of New Jersey, Veterans' Laws

Who Follow the Flag

All day long in the city's canyon-street,
With its populous cliffs alive on either side,
I saw a river of marching men like a tide
Flowing after the flag: and the rhythmic beat
Of the drums, and the bugle's resonant blare
Metred the tramp, tramp, tramp of a myriad feet,
While the red-white-and-blue was fluttering every-
        where
And the heart of the crowd kept time to a martial air.

    Millions have come across the sea
    To find beneath thy shelter room to grow;

Millions were born beneath thy folds to know
No other flag but thee;

    And other, darker millions bore the yoke
    Of bondage till the voice
    Of Lincoln spoke,
    And sent thee forth to set the bondman free.

Rejoice, dear flag, rejoice!
Since thou hast proved and passed that bitter strife,
Purer thy white through sacrificial life,
Brighter thy blue wherein new stars are set.
Thou art become a sign,
Revealed in heaven to speak of things divine:

    Of truth that dares
    To slay the lie it sheltered unawares;

Of courage fearless in the fight
Yet ever quick its foemen to forgive;

>Of conscience earnest to maintain its right
>And gladly grant the same to all who live.

Look forth across thy widespread lands,
O flag, and let thy stars tonight be eyes
To see the visionary hosts
Of men and women grateful to be thine,
That joyfully arise
From all thy borders and thy coasts
And follow after thee in endless line!
They lift to thee a forest of saluting hands;
They hail thee with a rolling ocean roar
Of cheers; and as the echo dies,
There comes a sweet and moving song
Of treble voices from the childish throng
Who run to thee from every school house door.

>Behold thine army! Here thy power lies:
>The men whom freedom has made strong,
>And bound to follow thee by willing vows,

The women greatened by thy joys
Of motherhood to rule a happy house;

>The vigorous girls and boys,
>Whose eager faces and unclouded brows
>Foretell the future of a nobler race
>Rich in the wealth of wisdom and true worth!

My vision darkens as the night descends:
And through the mystic atmosphere
I feel the creeping coldness that portends

A change of spirit in my dream.
The multitude that moved with song and cheer
Have vanished, yet a living stream
Flows on and follows still the flag,
But silent now, with leaden feet that lag
And falter in the deepening gloom,
A weird battalion bringing up the rear.
Ah, who are these in whom the vital bloom
Of life has withered to the dust of doom?
These little pilgrims prematurely worn
And bent as if they bore the weight of years,
These childish faces pallid and forlorn,
Too dull for laughter and too hard for tears?

    They are not girls and boys,
    But little "hands" who blindly, dumbly feed
    With their own blood the hungry god of Greed.

Are these the regiments that Freedom rears
To serve her cause in coming years?
Nay, every life that Avarice doth maim
And beggar in the helpless days of youth,
Shall surely claim
A just revenge, and take it without ruth.

    And every soul denied the right to grow
    Beneath the flag, shall be its secret foe.

Bow down, dear land, in penitence and shame!
Remember now thine oath, so nobly sworn,

    To guard an equal lot
    For every child within thy borders born!

Look up, look up ye downcast eyes!
The night is almost gone:
Along the new horizon flies
The banner of the dawn;
The eastern sky is banded low
With crimson bars;
While, far above the morning, glow
The everlasting stars.

O bright flag, O brave flag, O flag to lead the
   free!
The hand of God thy colors blent,
And heaven to earth thy glory lent,
To shield the weak and guide the strong,
To make an end of human wrong,
And draw a countless human host to follow after
   thee.

—*Henry Van Dyke*

Ode on Science *

The morning sun shines from the east,
And spreads his glories to the west.
All nations with his beams are blest,
Where'er his radiant light appears.
So science spreads her lighted ray
O'er lands which long in darkness lay;

She visits fair Columbia
And sets her sons among the stars.
Fair Freedom, her attendant waits,
To bless the portals of her gates,
To crown the young and rising States
With laurels of immortal day!
The British yoke, the Gallic chain,
Was urged upon our necks in vain;
All haughty tyrants we disdain,
And shout, "Long Live America!"
Shout, "Long Live America!"

—*Jezaniah Sumner*

* THE MUSIC FOR THIS SONG IS TO BE FOUND IN *A Treasury of American Song* (SECOND EDITION, PAGE 71), EDITED BY OLIN DOWNES AND ELIE SIEGMEISTER, PUBLISHED BY ALFRED A. KNOPF, INC., NEW YORK.

The Coming American

Bring me men to match my mountains,
Bring me men to match my plains,
And new eras in their brains.
Bring me men to match my prairies,
Men to match my inland seas,
Men whose thoughts shall pave a highway
Up to ampler destinies,
Pioneers to cleanse thought's marshlands,
　　　And to cleanse old error's fen;

Bring me men to match my mountains—
    Bring me men!

Bring me men to match my forests,
Strong to fight the storm and blast,
Branching toward the skyey future,
Rooted in the fertile past.
Bring me men to match my valleys,
    Tolerant of rain and snow,
Men within whose fruitful purpose
    Time's consummate blooms shall grow,
Men to tame the tigerish instincts
    Of the lair and cave and den,
Cleanse the dragon slime of nature—
    Bring me men!

Bring me men to match my rivers,
    Continent cleansers, flowing free,
Drawn by an eternal madness,
    To be mingled with the sea—
Men of oceanic impulse,
    Men whose moral currents sweep
Toward the wide, infolding ocean
    Of an undiscovered deep—
Men who feel the strong pulsation
    Of the central sea, and then
Time their currents by its earth throbs—
    Bring me Men.

                    —*Sam Walter Foss*

What the Flag Betokens

WHAT'S A FLAG? What's the love of country for which it stands? Maybe it begins with love of the land itself. It is the storied Mississippi rolling swift and muddy past St. Louis, rolling past Cairo, pouring down past the levees of New Orleans. It is lazy noontide in the pines of Carolina, it is a sea of wheat rippling in western Kansas, it is the San Francisco peaks far north across the glowing nakedness of Arizona.

> It is the Grand Canyon and a little stream coming down out of a New England ridge, in which are trout.

It is men at work. It is storm-tossed fishermen coming into Gloucester and Providence and Astoria. It is the farmer riding his great machine in the dust of harvest. It is the servants of fire in the murky splendor of Pittsburgh, between the Allegheny and the Monongahela, the trucks rumbling through the night, the locomotive engineer bringing the train in on time.

> It is the clerk in the office, the housewife doing the dishes and sending the children off to school.

It is small things remembered, the little corners of the land, the houses, the people that each one loves. We love our country because there was a little tree on a hill, and grass thereon, and a sweet valley below. It is voices that are remembered only, no longer heard. It is parents, friends, the lazy chat of street and store and office, and the ease of mind that makes life tranquil.

These are flesh of our flesh, bone of our bone, blood of our blood, a lasting part of what we are, each of us and all of us together.

It is stories told. It is the Pilgrims dying in their first dreadful winter. It is the minute man standing his ground at Concord Bridge, and dying there. It is the army in rags, sick, freezing, starving at Valley Forge. It is the wagons and the men on foot going westward over the Cumberland Gap, floating down the great rivers, rolling over the great plains. It is the settler hacking fiercely at the primeval forest on his new, his own lands. It is Thoreau at Walden Pond, Lincoln at Cooper Union, and Lee riding home from Appomattox.

It is corruption and disgrace, answered always by men who would not let the flag lie in the dust, who have stood up in every generation to fight for the old ideals and the old rights, at risk of ruin or life itself.

It is a great multitude of people on pilgrimage, common and ordinary people, charged with the usual human failings, yet filled with such a hope as never caught the imaginations and the hearts of any nation on earth before.

The hope of liberty. The hope of justice. The hope of a land in which a man can stand straight, without fear, without rancor.

The land and the people and the flag—the land a continent, the people of every race, the flag a symbol of what humanity may aspire to when the wars are over and the barriers are down.

To these each generation must be dedicated and consecrated anew, to defend with life itself, if need be, but, above all, in friendliness, in hope, in courage, to live for.

—*The New York Times*

Closing Ceremony

ON THIS ANNIVERSARY of the adoption of our national banner, we have endeavored to bring to mind all its solemn and sacred meanings. May we be ever aware of the noble purposes and deeds, the valor and heroism, the devotion to freedom and justice that have made our flag sacred. Let us renew today our pledge of allegiance to the flag and to the sacred ideals for which it stands. May we never make of it a mere fetish, nor of our salute to it an act of blind idolatry that commits us to nothing but national self-pride and self-will. But let our salute to it be a token of reverence for the spiritual ideals of our people, a self dedication to a national life that advances the cause of God's kingdom of freedom and love.

133

*The assembly rises and in unison pledges allegiance
to the flag in the following words:*

I pledge allegiance to the flag of the United States
of America and to the republic for which it stands, one
nation indivisible, with liberty and justice for all.

All join in singing the national anthem,
THE STAR-SPANGLED BANNER

Oh, say, can you see, by the dawn's early light,
What so proudly we hailed at the twilight's last gleam-
  ing,
Whose broad stripes and bright stars thro' the peril-
  ous fight,
O'er the ramparts we watch'd, were so gallantly
  streaming?
And the rockets' red glare, the bombs bursting in air
Gave proof thro' the night that our flag was still there.
Oh, say, does that Star-spangled Banner still wave
O'er the land of the free and the home of the brave!

On the shore, dimly seen thro' the mists of the deep,
Where the foe's haughty host in dread silence reposes,
What is that which the breeze o'er the towering steep,
As it fitfully blows, half conceals half discloses?
Now it catches the gleam of the morning's first beam,
In full glory reflected now shines on the stream.
'Tis the Star-spangled Banner, oh, long may it wave
O'er the land of the free and the home of the brave!

Oh, thus be it ever when free men shall stand
Between their loved homes and the war's desolation!

134

Blest with vict'ry and peace, may the heav'n rescued
      land
Praise the pow'r that hath made and preserved us a
      nation!
Then conquer we must, when our cause it is just,
And this be our motto: "In God is our trust!"
And the Star-spangled Banner in triumph shall wave
O'er the land of the free and the home of the brave!

—*Francis Scott Key*

JULY 4

INDEPENDENCE

DAY

A Day Devoted to Reflections on the Uses of Freedom

The Significance of the Day

OUR FATHERS' GOD, Author of Liberty, who desirest that all men be free to serve Thee and that none be constrained to serve other masters, we thank Thee for the liberty that our nation achieved in the war for independence. Thou hast endowed all men equally with the right to life, to liberty, and to the pursuit of happiness. Teach us to respect the rights of others and to assert our own rights in accordance with Thy will. May we never abuse our liberties by employing them to our own advantage while depriving others of the opportunity to realize their just desires and hopes.

May we never forfeit our liberties by permitting our minds to be enslaved to error, superstition, or prejudice, or our wills to yield to the promptings of cowardice or self-indulgence. May we ever expand the area of human freedom by developing to the utmost and using for the good of all whatever powers Thou hast bestowed upon us. Let us ever cherish our nation's independence and the freedom of its institutions, so that our nation may serve Thee and Thy law of love and justice. AMEN.

Prayer That America Fulfill the Promise of Its Founding

O GOD, who art Liberator and Redeemer, Lawgiver and Judge, who rulest over all mankind and presidest over the destinies of nations, we invoke Thy continued blessing on our Republic, which Thy grace called into being and Thy love has sustained to this day.

> May America remain loyal to the principles of the Declaration of Independence and apply them to ever widening areas of life.

Keep us from all manner of oppression, persecution, and unjust discrimination; save us from religious, racial, and class conflicts; preserve our country as a haven of refuge for the victims of injustice and misrule.

> Instruct us in the art of living together. Teach us to respect differences, to reconcile clashing interests, and to help one another achieve a harmonious and abundant life.

Give us the wisdom to choose honest and capable leaders who will govern us according to Thy law of righteousness.

> Bless Thou the enterprise of the American people, that they may utilize the resources of the land for the good of all men.

May our nation be ever receptive to new revelations of truth in science and philosophy, ever sensitive to the appeal of beauty in nature and art, ever responsive to the call of duty and the spirit of religious consecration and worship;

And may Americans so love their country that they shall withhold no sacrifice required to safeguard its life and to fulfill its promise.

—*Jewish Reconstructionist Foundation,*
SABBATH PRAYER BOOK

Once to Every Man and Nation *

Once to ev'ry man and nation
Comes the moment to decide,
In the strife of truth with falsehood,
For the good or evil side;
Some great cause, God's new Messiah,
Off'ring each the bloom or blight,
And the choice goes by forever
'Twixt that darkness and that light.

Then to side with truth is noble,
When we share her wretched crust,
Ere her cause bring fame and profit,
And 'tis prosp'rous to be just;
Then it is the brave man chooses
While the coward stands aside
Till the multitude make virtue
Of the faith they had denied.

Though the cause of evil prosper
Yet 'tis truth alone is strong;
Though her portion be the scaffold,
And upon the throne be wrong,
Yet that scaffold sways the future,
And, behind the dim unknown,
Standeth God within the shadow
Keeping watch above His own.

—*James Russell Lowell*

*THE MUSIC FOR THIS POEM IS TO BE FOUND IN *Assembly Songs and Choruses* (PAGE 105), EDITED BY RANDALL J. CONDON, HELEN S. LEAVITT, AND ELBRIDGE W. NEWTON, PUBLISHED BY GINN AND COMPANY, BOSTON.

On Non-Cooperation with Tyrannical Governments

IT WAS THE MERIT of our fathers who declared the independence of the thirteen colonies from British rule that they would not submit to tyranny even when it was backed by all the prestige of the state, and had the military power at its command.

Let us their sons resolve to retain our loyalty to the sacred and equal rights of men.

Whenever the state violates those rights, it is not only the privilege but the duty of the citizen to refuse to abet the unjust encroachment of tyrannical authority.

> Let him not be cowed by the power at the state's disposal; a greater Power than that of the state will uphold his defiance.

A state that is tyrannical and oppressive cannot bear the disdain with which the brave and true withdraw from any share in her unreasoning brutality; so she shuts them behind prison walls away from her sight.

> But behind those walls they know themselves freer than those without who submit to the tyrants and help carry out their evil designs.

On that honorable ground where the tyrannical state places those who are not *with* her but *against* her, all whom the despotic power could not make bow to its will meet as equals and brothers.

> In a slave state the prison is the only house in which a freeman can abide with honor.

Think not that your voice can no longer plead your cause when you are penned in a cell by those who would stifle it; that then they can shut their ears to its piercing barbs.

> Truth is stronger than error, and never is its strength more potent against injustice than when wielded by one who chooses to suffer wrong rather than aid in inflicting it on others.

143

The honest man always casts his vote for the right as he sees it. Let the vote we cast be no mere slip of paper but the whole influence of all that we are.

> When subjects refuse allegiance to a tyrannical government, and decent men refuse to fill any of its offices, then is its overthrow assured.

Even if bleed we must for our refusal to carry out an evil and oppressive decree, let that not deter us.

> When the conscience is wounded, the spirit bleeds; all one's manhood and immortality bleed to death.

What folly it is for tyrants to pen men within walls of stones and lock them behind doors!

> Do they think that men are mere flesh and blood? Do they know nothing of the souls of men?

Is this the best use they can make of citizens who desire that life shall be fair and free, that men shall be equal and be helpful one to another?

> A barrier thicker than that of any dungeon wall shuts out the tyrant from the freedom of those who do not fear to think truth and to do right.

What a waste of stone and mortar are the walls that we raise to hem in the movements of those who challenge tyranny.

> The imprisoned are visited by thoughts no locked door can bar, and their meditations escape and range freely abroad.

The spirit of the free man baffles all wielders of despotic authority; he is forever beyond reach of their power to compel.

Unable to move *him,* they punish *his body,* as one afraid to fight a strong man may kick at his dog.

The tyrant state is half-witted; it knows not its friends from its foes.

Instead of respect it earns contempt; it is to be pitied for its stupid blundering.

The foundation of the state must ever be respect for the individual; it must revere the image of God in its citizens.

Only then will it have their wholehearted allegiance, and be strong with the strength of man's indomitable spirit.

—*Adapted from Henry David Thoreau,*
CIVIL DISOBEDIENCE

Men, Whose Boast It Is *

Men, whose boast it is that ye
Come of fathers brave and free,
If there breathe on earth a slave,
Are ye truly free and brave?
If ye do not feel the chain
When it works a brother's pain,
Are ye not base slaves indeed,
Slaves unworthy to be freed?

Is true freedom but to break
Fetters for our own dear sake,
And with leathern hearts forget
That we owe mankind a debt?
No! true freedom is to share
All the chains our brothers wear,
And, with heart and hand, to be
Earnest to make others free.

They are slaves who fear to speak
For the fallen and the weak;
They are slaves who will not choose
Hatred, scoffing, and abuse,
Rather than in silence shrink
From the truth they needs must think;
They are slaves who dare not be
In the right with two or three. Amen.

—*James Russell Lowell*

* THE MUSIC FOR THIS POEM IS TO BE FOUND IN *Hymns for
the Living Age* (PAGE 289), EDITED BY H. AUGUSTINE SMITH,
PUBLISHED BY THE FLEMING H. REVELL COMPANY, NEW YORK.

Declaration of Independence

On the fourth of July, in the year 1776, a new nation was born, the United States of America, conceived in liberty and dedicated to the proposition that all men are created equal. Their faith and vision the Founding Fathers expressed in a solemn Declaration of Independence. That Declaration set forth the principles which moved them to establish the former British colonies as an independent union of states. It is well that on the anniversary of this event we be reminded of the spiritual foundations of our Republic, and that we renew from year to year our allegiance to them. Let us then rise and listen to the words of that epoch-making Declaration.

The assembly rises

WE HOLD THESE TRUTHS TO BE SELF-EVIDENT: that all men are created equal; that they are endowed by their Creator with certain unalienable rights; that among these are life, liberty and the pursuit of happiness; that to secure these rights, governments are instituted among men, deriving their just powers from the consent of the governed; that whenever any form of government becomes destructive of these ends, it is the right of the people to alter or to abolish it, and to institute new government, laying its foundation on such principles and organizing its powers in such form, as to them shall seem most likely to effect their safety and happiness. . . .

"We, therefore, the representatives of the United States of America, in general congress assembled, appealing to the Supreme Judge of the world for the rectitude of our intentions, do, in the name, and by the authority of the good people of these colonies, solemnly publish and declare that these United Colonies are, and of right ought to be, free and independent States. . . . And for the support of this Declaration, with a firm reliance on the protection of Divine Providence, we mutually pledge to each other our lives, our fortune and our sacred honor."

The assembly is seated

The Universal Significance of American Devotion to Liberty

THE DECLARATION OF INDEPENDENCE holds a great promise for all mankind. In that solemn declaration, the Founding Fathers spoke and acted, not for a class, but for a people.

It is for us, their descendants, to make it understood that they spoke and acted, not for one people only, but for all.

They consciously planned that men of every class should be free, that America should be a place to which people of every nation might resort who wished to share with them the rights and privileges of free men.

In loyalty to their example, let us plan together, with men of every nation, to make not only the liberties of America secure but the liberties of every other people as well. . . .

Let us seek to establish everywhere the reign of law, based upon the consent of the governed and sustained by the organized opinion of mankind,

That the promise of the Declaration of Independence may be fulfilled in a brotherhood of free peoples throughout the world.

—Adapted from Woodrow Wilson

Ode to the Fourth of July *

'Tis done, the edict past, by Heaven decreed,
And Hancock's name confirms the glorious deed.
On this auspicious morn was Independence born:
Propitious day!
Hail the United States of blest America!

CHORUS

Fly! Fly! Fly, swift winged Fame,
The news, the news proclaim.
From shore to shore, let cannons roar,
And joyful voices shout Columbia's name.
Shout! Shout! Columbia's name, Columbia's name.

See haughty Britain sending hosts of foes,
With vengeance armed our freedom to oppose.
But Washington, the great, dispelled impending fate,
And spurned each plan.
Americans combine to hail the godlike man.

CHORUS

—*Daniel George*

* THE MUSIC FOR THIS SONG IS TO BE FOUND IN *A Treasury of American Song* (SECOND EDITION, PAGE 68), EDITED BY OLIN DOWNES AND ELIE SIEGMEISTER, PUBLISHED BY ALFRED A. KNOPF, INC., NEW YORK.

Religious Implications of the Democratic Idea

THE DEMOCRATIC IDEA of equal human rights is founded in human nature, and comes from the nature of God, who made human nature.

To carry out that idea politically is to execute justice, which is the will of God.

The fulfillment of this idea calls for a government of all, for all, by all.

It asks that political power be in all hands, property in all hands, wisdom in all heads, goodness in all hearts, religion in all souls.

True religion makes a man self-respectful, earnest, and faithful to the infinite God.

It disposes him to give all men their rights, and to claim his own rights at all times; its inner essence is piety and its outer manifestation is goodness.

In a democracy the aim of Law is to give justice to all men, and the first task of government is the establishment of justice.

To equalize opportunity, a democracy founds schools for all; looks after those who are most in need; defends and protects the feeblest as well as the richest and most powerful.

The democratic state is for the individual, and for all the individuals; it balances in the scales of justice the rights of all and the interests of all.

It demands free speech; everything is open to examination and discussion.

Thought is to be free, speech to be free, work to be free, and worship to be free.

Such is the democratic idea, affirmed in our Declaration of Independence; let us affirm it also in the daily life of our people.

—Adapted from Theodore Parker,
THE STATE OF THE UNION

Lift Every Voice and Sing*

Lift every voice and sing, till earth and heaven ring,
Ring with the harmonies of liberty;
Let our rejoicing rise, high as the list'ning skies,
Let it resound loud as the rolling sea.

Sing a song full of the faith that the dark past has
   taught us.
Sing a song full of the hope that the present has
   brought us;
Facing the rising sun of our new day begun,
Let us march on till victory is won.

Stony the road we trod, bitter the chastening rod,
Felt in the days when hope unborn had died;
Yet with a steady beat, have not our weary feet
Come to the place for which our fathers sighed?

We have come over a way that with tears has been
   watered;
We have come, treading our path through the flood
   of the slaughtered;
Out from the gloomy past, 'til now we stand at last
Where the white gleam of our bright star is cast.

God of our weary years, God of our silent tears,
Thou who hast brought us thus far on the way;
Thou who hast by Thy might led us into the light,
Keep us forever in Thy path, we pray.

Lest our feet stray from the places, our God, where
     we met Thee,
Lest, our hearts drunk with the wine of the world, we
     forget Thee;
Shadowed beneath Thy hand, may we forever stand,
True to our God, true to our native land.

—*James Weldon Johnson*

* THE MUSIC FOR THIS SONG IS TO BE FOUND IN *Git on Board*
(PAGE 16), EDITED BY BEATRICE LANDECK, PUBLISHED BY THE
EDWARD B. MARKS MUSIC CORPORATION, NEW YORK.

Statute of Virginia for Religious Freedom

> *America cherishes its liberties not primarily for
> the opportunity that they afford to achieve pros-
> perity or comfort but for the opportunity that
> they afford to be faithful to conscience. It is sig-
> nificant that the author of our Declaration of
> Independence was also the author of that other
> great document of American freedom, the Statute
> of Virginia for Religious Freedom. It is well,
> therefore, that, on this day on which we read
> from our Declaration of Independence, we read
> also from that other sacred document.*

WHEREAS Almighty God hath created the mind
free; that all attempts to influence it by temporal pun-

153

ishments or burthens, or by civil incapacitations, tend only to beget habits of hypocrisy and meanness, and are a departure from the plan of the Holy Author of our religion, who being Lord both of body and mind, yet chose not to propagate it by coercions on either, as was in His almighty power to do. . . .

Be it enacted by the General Assembly, that no man shall be compelled to frequent or support any religious worship, place, or ministry whatsoever, nor shall be enforced, restrained, molested, or burthened in his body or goods, nor shall otherwise suffer on account of his religious opinions or belief; but that all men shall be free to profess, and by argument to maintain their opinion in matters of religion, and that the same shall in no wise diminish, enlarge, or affect their civil capacities.

A Holy Nation

Let Liberty run onward with the years,
And circle with the seasons: let her break
The tyrant's harshness, the oppressor's spears;

    Bring ripened recompenses that shall make
    Supreme amends for sorrow's long arrears;

Drop holy benison on hearts that ache;
Put clearer radiance into human eyes,

    And set the glad earth singing to the skies.

Clean natures coin pure statutes. Let us cleanse
The hearts that beat within us.

Let us mow
Clear to the roots our falseness and pretence.

Tread down our rank ambitions, overthrow
Our braggart moods of puffed self-consequence,

Plough up our hideous thistles which do grow
Faster than maize in May time, and strike dead
The base infections our low greeds have bred.

—*Richard Realf*

Franklin D. Roosevelt's
Tribute to Thomas Jefferson

WHEN WE READ of the patriots of 1776 and the
fathers of the Constitution, we are taken into the presence of men who caught the fire of greatness from one
another, and all became elevated above the common
run of mankind. The source of their greatness was the
stirring of a new sense of freedom. Theirs were not
the gods of things as they were, but the gods of things
as they ought to be. They used new means and new
models to build new structures.

Farmer, lawyer, mechanic, scientist, architect, philosopher, statesman, Jefferson encompassed the full scope of the knowledge of his time, and his life was one of rich diversity. He was a great gentleman. He was a great commoner. The two are not incompatible.

Shortly before taking office as President of the United States, he wrote to a friend, "I have sworn on the Altar of God eternal hostility against every form of tyranny over the mind of man." His life served that consecration.

On one day in his long life he gave to the world a Declaration of Independence on behalf of political freedom for himself and his fellow Americans. But his Declaration of Independence for the human mind was a continuing achievement, renewed and reiterated every day that he lived.

One hundred and sixty years have passed since the Fourth of July, 1776. Through all the intervening years America has lived and grown under the system of government established by Jefferson and his generation.

Democracy needs now, as it found then, men developed to the limit of their capacity, through education, for ultimate responsibility. Emergencies and decisions in our individual and community and national lives are the stuff out of which national character is made.

Was the spirit of such men as Jefferson the spirit of a Golden Age gone now and never to be repeated in our history? Was the feeling of fundamental freedom which lighted the fire of their ability a miracle we shall never see again?

That is not my belief. It is not beyond our power to relight that sacred fire. There are no limitations upon the nation's capacity to obtain and maintain true freedom except the strength of our nation's desire and determination.

Jefferson was given many high offices in State and Nation. But the words recorded above his grave, chosen by himself, are only these:

"HERE WAS BURIED THOMAS JEFFERSON, AUTHOR OF THE DECLARATION OF AMERICAN INDEPENDENCE, OF THE STATUTE OF VIRGINIA FOR RELIGIOUS FREEDOM, AND FATHER OF THE UNIVERSITY OF VIRGINIA."

The honors other men had given him were unimportant; the opportunities he had given other men to become free were all that really counted.

Jefferson and Liberty*

The gloomy night before us flies,
The reign of terror now is o'er;
Its gags, inquisitors, and spies,
Its herds of harpies are no more!

CHORUS
Rejoice! Columbia's sons, rejoice!
To tyrants never bend the knee,
But join with heart, and soul, and voice,
For Jefferson and Liberty.

No lordling here, with gorging jaws,
Shall wring from industry the food;
Nor fiery bigot's holy laws
Lay waste our fields and streets in blood!
CHORUS

Here strangers from a thousand shores,
Compelled by tyranny to roam,
Shall find, amidst abundant stores,
A nobler and a happier home.
CHORUS

Here Art shall lift her laurel's head,
Wealth, Industry, and Peace divine;
And where dark, pathless forests spread,
Rich fields and lofty cities shine.
CHORUS

From Europe's wants and woes remote,
A friendly waste of waves between,
Here plenty cheers the humblest cot,
And smiles on every village-green.
CHORUS

Here, free as air, expanded space,
To every soul and sect shall be—
That sacred privilege of our race—
The worship of the Deity.
CHORUS

Let foes to freedom dread the name;
But should they touch the sacred tree,
Twice fifty thousand swords would flame
For Jefferson and Liberty.
CHORUS

From Georgia to Lake Champlain,
From seas to Mississippi's shore,
Ye sons of Freedom, loud proclaim—
"The reign of terror is no more."
CHORUS

—*Anonymous*

* THE MUSIC FOR THIS SONG IS TO BE FOUND IN *A Treasury of American Song* (SECOND EDITION, PAGE 80), EDITED BY OLIN DOWNES AND ELIE SIEGMEISTER, PUBLISHED BY ALFRED A. KNOPF, INC., NEW YORK.

Hymn for the Fourth of July

Before the Lord we bow,
	The God who reigns above,
And rules the world below,
	Boundless in power and love.
		Our thanks we bring,
		In joy and praise,
		Our hearts we raise,
		To Heaven's bright King.

The nation thou hast blest
	May well thy love declare,
From foes and fears at rest,
	Protected by thy care.
		For this fair land,
		For this bright day,
		Our thanks we pay,
		Gifts of thy hand.

Our fathers sought thee, Lord,
  And on thy help relied;
Thou heardest, and gavest the word,
  And all their needs supplied.
      Led by thy hand
      To victory,
      They hailed a free
      And rescued land.

God of our lives! that hand
  Be now as then displayed,
To give this favored land
  Thy never-failing aid.
      Still may it be
      Thy fixed abode!
      Be thou our God,
      Thy people we.

May every mountain height,
  Each vale and forest green,
Shine in thy word's pure light,
  And its rich fruits be seen!
      May every tongue
      Be tuned to praise,
      And join to raise
      A grateful song.

                —*Francis Scott Key*

Closing Prayer

ALMIGHTY GOD, who hast given us this good land for our heritage, we humbly beseech Thee that we may always prove ourselves a people mindful of Thy favor and glad to do Thy will. Bless our land with honorable industry, sound learning, and pure manners. Save us from violence, discord, and confusion, from pride and arrogance, and from every evil way. Defend our liberties and fashion into one united people the multitudes brought hither, of many kindreds and tongues.

Endow with the spirit of wisdom those to whom, in Thy name, we entrust the authority of government, that there may be peace and justice at home; and that, through obedience to Thy law, we may show forth Thy praise among the nations of the earth.

In the time of prosperity, fill our hearts with thankfulness; in the day of trouble, suffer not our trust in Thee to fail. AMEN.

—*Colgate Divinity School*

FIRST MONDAY IN SEPTEMBER

LABOR

DAY

A Day Devoted to Reflection on the Role
of Labor in Shaping a Better World

The Significance of the Day

OUR GOD AND CREATOR:

On this day we consecrate to Thee the labor of muscle and mind. We thank Thee for the gifts of life and for the wherewithal to sustain it. Thine is the earth and all it holds, and Thou hast unlocked its resources for the service of man. Thine is the energy pent in the seed, and Thine is the strength and skill of man, whereby he causes the fields to yield him food in abundance.

When men bring forth that which satisfies their needs, it is Thou who instructest them. When they exchange with one another what they can best do and make, it is Thou who guidest them. Thou desirest that all men have at their disposal what each most needs for health and comfort and for the full use of the gifts wherewith Thou hast endowed him.

Bless our toil, O God, that no one in this land of ours or in any other land need ever lack bread to eat, or raiment to wear, the shelter of a home, or whatever else he may require for health of body and mind.

Restrain our hungers from becoming extravagant, and hold back our desires from exceeding the bounds of reason and justice.

Withhold us from selling our labor to the service of greed and of hate, and give us the wisdom and courage to devote it to Thy service, to banish poverty, disease, and war, and to establish Thy rule of freedom, brotherhood, and peace. AMEN.

Spiritual Conditions for a Productive Society

LET THIS BE THE GOAL of our American Society—to achieve a rich and full life in which all share and play their parts,

> In which all toil with hand or brain to produce the goods that are needed and all share equitably the goods that are produced.

That is the American dream. To realize it, the spiritual and intellectual life of our society must be higher than any which has been attained.

> There must be no segregated classes, no groups dominated, each by its own separate interests, with habits, markets, arts, and ways of living that are exclusively its own.

If that dream cannot be fulfilled, nothing is left us but frustrating conflict.

> We will be plunged into a deadly strife of individual against individual and class against class.

If the dream is to come true, those on top, financially, intellectually, or otherwise, must devote themselves to the "Great Society," to the service of the common interests of the entire community.

And those below must strive to rise, not merely in wealth but in wisdom, refinement, and virtue.

We cannot become a great democracy by giving ourselves up as individuals to selfishness, physical comfort, and cheap amusements.

To achieve a better and richer life for all demands that each shall be capable of wanting to share in it.

It can never be wrought into a reality by people whose ambition is roused by petty rivalries and who covet the success and prestige of neighbors.

Wealth by itself or prestige by itself is nothing; all depends on what is made of each.

Lincoln was not great because he was born in a log cabin, but because he got out of it—because he rose above poverty and ignorance.

Contentment with mean things and low aims keep thousands in the huts where they were born and are a drag on the whole community, depressing its standard of achievement.

—*Suggested by James Truslow Adams,*
THE EPIC OF AMERICA

The Farmer-Labor Train *

From the high Canadian Rockies to that land of
    Mexico,
The city and the country, wherever you may go,
Through the wild and windy weather, the sun, the sleet
    and rain
Comes a-whistling through the country, this Farmer-
    Labor Train.

Oh, listen to the jingle, the rumble and the roar,
She's a rolling through New England to the West Pa-
    cific Shore,
It's a long time we been waiting, now she's whistling
    round the bend,
Now we'll ride into the White House on that Farmer-
    Labor Train.

There's lumberjacks, and teamsters, and sailors from
    the sea,
And there's farming boys from Texas and the hills of
    Tennessee,
There's miners from Kentucky, and there's fishermen
    from Maine,
Every worker in the country rides that Farmer-Labor
    Train.

There's warehouse boys and truckers, and guys that
    skin the cats,
The men that run the steel mills, the furnace and the
    blasts;

Through the smoky factory cities, o'er the hot and
    dusty plains,
And the cushions they are crowded on this Farmer-
    Labor Train.

There are folks of every color, and they're sitting side
    by side,
From the swamps of Louisiana and across the Great
    Divide;
From the wheat fields and the orchards and the lowing
    cattle range,
And they're calling on to victory on this Farmer-Labor
    Train.

This train pulled into Washington one bright and
    happy day;
When she steamed into the station you could hear the
    people say,
"There's that Farmer-Labor Special, she's full of
    union men,
And they're headed for the White House on that
    Farmer-Labor Train."

Yes, the crooked politicians, they knew their time has
    come,
'Cause the union men and women put the gamblers on
    the run,
They sealed them in a boxcar, and switched them off
    the main,
And they cleared the people's railroad track for the
    Farmer-Labor Train.

                    —*Woody Guthrie*

* THE MUSIC FOR THIS SONG IS TO BE FOUND IN *The People's
Song Book* (PAGE 85), EDITED BY WALDEMAR HILLE, PUB-
LISHED BY BONI & GAER, INC., NEW YORK.

Labor, the Shaper of Civilization

All civilizations are the product of man's labor applied to the resources of nature. The axe that clears the primeval forest for the habitation of man is a significant symbol of the creative role of labor. That thought is expressed in Walt Whitman's Song of the Broad Axe, *from which the following selection is taken.*

The axe leaps!

The shapes arise!
Shapes of the using of axes, and the users and all that
      neighbors them,
Cutters down of wood and haulers of it to the Pe-
      nobscot or Kennebec,
Dwellers in cabins among the Californian mountains
      or by the little lakes, or on the Columbia . . .
Seal-fishers, whalers, arctic seamen breaking passages
      through the ice.

The shapes arise!
Shapes of factories, arsenals, foundries, markets,
Shapes of the two-threaded tracks of railroads . . .
Ship-yards and dry-docks . . .
The ships themselves on their ways . . .

The shapes arise!
The shape measur'd, saw'd, jack'd, join'd, stain'd . . .
The shape of the planks of the family home, the home
      of the friendly parents and children,
The shape of the roof of the home of the happy young
      man and woman, the roof over the well-
      married young man and woman,

The roof over the supper joyously cook'd by the chaste
          wife, and joyously eaten by the chaste hus-
          band, content after his day's work.

The main shapes arise!
Shapes of Democracy total, result of centuries,
Shapes ever projecting other shapes,
Shapes of turbulent manly cities,
Shapes of the friends and home-givers of the whole
          earth,
Shapes bracing the earth and braced with the whole
          earth.

The Labor Movement as an Instrument for the Elevation of Mankind

LABOR DAY IS A GOOD DAY to rest the hands
and give the brain a chance—to think about what has
been, and is, and is yet to be. The workingman is the
only man to whom we should take off our hats. As we
salute him, we honor ourselves.

The workingman has given us what we have, has
made us what we are, and will make us what we
hope to be.

Like the rough-hewn stone from which the noble statue is chiseled by the hand of man, the Toiler is the rough-hewn bulk, from which the perfect Man is being chiseled by the hand of God.

All the workingmen of the earth are necessary to the whole Workingman—and he alone will survive of all the human race.

The way of Labor's progress has been long and weary and full of pain, and many have fallen by the wayside,

But the unconquerable army of Labor is still on the march and as it looks ahead, it beholds upon the horizon the first glowing rays of the social sunrise.

Courage, comrades! The struggle must be won, for Peace will come only when she comes hand in hand with Freedom.

We are all one—all workers of all lands and climes. We are one, regardless of color, creed, or sex.

And by our unity we shall prevail, the solidarity of Labor will vanquish slavery and humanize the world.

—Adapted from Engene V. Debs,
LABOR DAY GREETING

Union Train*

Oh, what is that
I see yonder coming?
Oh, what is that
I see yonder coming?
Oh, what is that
I see yonder coming?

Well, it's that union train a-coming.
It has saved many a thousand
It will save many a thousand more.

It will carry us to freedom
We're fighting for our freedom
Black and white together.

—*Almanac Singers*

*THE MUSIC FOR THIS SONG IS TO BE FOUND IN *The People's Song Book* (PAGE 84), EDITED BY WALDEMAR HILLE, PUBLISHED BY BONI & GAER, INC., NEW YORK.

The Labor Movement and Economic Justice

If labor is to build up an American civilization of which all of us can be proud, provision must be made for a just sharing in the responsibilities and rewards of labor. The movement of labor to achieve for the wage earner a fair wage, decent working conditions, and the protection of his human rights and human dignity is, in effect, a movement for the advancement of American civilization as a whole.

It is well, therefore, that on Labor Day we draw inspiration from the eloquent words of American champions of equality of economic opportunity.

One of these champions was Wendell Phillips. Answering what was intended as an indictment of the labor movement, the charge that it stood for equalization of property, he retorted substantially in the following words.

WELL, WE DO MEAN IT; . . . . What we need is an equalization of property—nothing else. My ideal of a civilization is a very high one, but the approach to it is a New England town of some two thousand inhabitants, with no rich man and no poor man in it, all mingling in the same society, every child at the same school, no poorhouse, no beggar, opportunities equal, nobody too proud to stand aloof, nobody too humble to be shut out. That's New England as it was fifty years ago. . . . But the civilization that lingers beautifully on the hillsides of New England, nestles sweetly in the valleys of Vermont, the moment it approaches a crowd like Boston, or a million of men gathered in one place like New York—rots. It cannot force the crowd; it cannot stand the great centres of modern civilization. . . .

What is our cause? It is this: there are three hundred and fifty millions of human beings in what is commonly called Christendom, and two hundred millions of them don't have enough to eat from January to December. I won't ask for culture, for opportunities for education, for travel, for society; but two hundred millions of men . . . don't have enough to eat. A hundred thousand men in the city of New York live in dwellings that a rich man wouldn't let his horse stay in a day. . . .

You say, "What does labor need in New England?" It needs justice. A gentleman in New York has recently bought a whole town; and he is going to build model houses, and house there all the labor he can get to go into them. Yet the civilization which alone can look God in the face is a civilization where one man does not depend on the pity of another man's building him a model lodging-house; the civilization which alone can look God in the face is a civilization where one man could not build, and another man would not need, that sort of refuge.

—*Adapted from Wendell Phillips,*
THE FOUNDATION OF THE LABOR MOVEMENT

The Dignity of Labor

OUR GOD AND CREATOR, Thou hast created Man in Thine image, endowing him with creative powers.

> Thou hast given him a resourceful mind and skillful hands wherewith he can dominate the world of nature; he can unlock its pent-up powers and make them serve his every want.

We thank Thee, O God, for the capacity to work wherein men are different from all other living beings.

> For these others survive by adjusting themselves to their environment, but man has survived by transforming his environment and adjusting it to himself.

Grant that we may never abuse those powers that give dignity to our work,

> That we may ever remember that our creativity is Thy gift, designed for Thy service, and that, when our plans conform not to Thy designs, the structures we create collapse over our heads.

Give us the humility and the wisdom to employ our labors only to just ends,

> To purposes from which all can benefit and from which none will suffer hurt.

Check in us the greed of acquisition and the lust of domination,

> That we may all enjoy the fruits of our toil without denying to any the fruits of theirs.

Let us never forget our dependence on one another and on that spirit of brotherhood which is a manifestation of Thy love.

> For each of us by himself is weak and helpless, and only our cooperation makes our work effective.

The tools that we use, the knowledge that we apply, the very bread that we eat, are not of our single creation but are the accumulated product of the toil and skill of many workers, over many generations.

> Inspire us therefore with loyalty to all who work and with the spirit of mutual helpfulness and brotherly love.

Give us the strength to produce abundantly, the justice to distribute equitably, and the wisdom and self-control to consume prudently the goods that satisfy our needs,

> That we may all know the joy of creativity, the thrill of comradeship, the zest of health, and the peace of mind that are the reward of human labor when it conforms with Thy divine will.

The Man with the Hoe

Labor Day stresses the importance and dignity of labor. But labor possesses dignity only when it is the toil of free men and is freely given in exchange for the goods that are necessary to a secure, healthy, and happy life. Labor Day must, therefore, also stress the protest against all forms of slavery, serfdom, and soul-destroying drudgery, which rob human life of its dignity.

The poet Edwin Markham saw in Millet's painting of the Man with the Hoe a symbol of the brutalization of the peasant who is compelled to toil under intolerably oppressive conditions. Listen, then, to the challenging poem which the contemplation of the lot of the Man with the Hoe evoked from this liberty-loving American poet.

Bowed by the weight of centuries he leans
Upon his hoe and gazes on the ground,
The emptiness of ages in his face
And on his back the burden of the world.
Who made him dead to rapture and despair,
A thing that grieves not and that never hopes,
Stolid and stunned, a brother to the ox?
Who loosened and let down this brutal jaw?
Whose was the hand that slanted back this brow?
Whose breath blew out the light within this brain?

Is this the Thing the Lord God made and gave
To have dominion over sea and land;
To trace the stars and search the heavens for power;
To feel the passion of Eternity?
Is this the Dream He dreamed who shaped the suns

And marked their ways upon the ancient deep?
Down all the stretch of Hell to its last gulf
There is no shape more terrible than this—
More tongued with censure of the world's blind
        greed—
More filled with signs and portents for the soul—
More fraught with danger to the universe.

What gulfs between him and the seraphim!
Slave of the wheel of labor, what to him
Are Plato and the swing of Pleiades?
What the long reaches of the peaks of song,
The rift of dawn, the reddening of the rose?
Through this dread shape the suffering ages look;
Time's tragedy is in that aching stoop;
Through this dread shape humanity betrayed,
Plundered, profaned and disinherited,
Cries protest to the Judges of the World,
A protest that is also prophecy.

O masters, lords and rulers in all lands,
Is this the handiwork you give to God,
This monstrous thing distorted and soul-quenched?
How will you ever straighten up this shape;
Touch it again with immortality;
Give back the upward looking and the light;
Rebuild in it the music and the dream;
Make right the immemorial infamies,
Perfidious wrongs, immedicable woes?

O masters, lords and rulers in all lands,
How will the Future reckon with this Man?
How answer his brute question in that hour
When whirlwinds of rebellion shake the world?

How will it be with kingdoms and with kings—
With those who shaped him to the thing he is—
When this dumb Terror shall reply to God,
After the silence of the centuries?

The Farmer Comes to Town *

When the farmer comes to town with his wagon
      broken down,
Oh, the farmer is the man who feeds them all.
If you'll only look and see, I think you will agree
That the farmer is the man who feeds them all.

CHORUS
The farmer is the man, the farmer is the man,
Lives on credit till the fall.
With the interest rate so high, it's a wonder he don't
      die,
For the mortgage man's the one who gets it all.

When the lawyer hangs around, while the butcher
      cuts a pound,
Oh the farmer is the man who feeds them all.

And the preacher and the cook go a-strolling by the
     brook,
Oh the farmer is the man who feeds them all.
                                       chorus

When the banker says he's broke, and the merchant's
     up in smoke,
They forget that it's the farmer feeds them all.
It would put them to the test if the farmer took a rest;
Then they'd know that it's the farmer feeds them all.
CHORUS

The farmer is the man, the farmer is the man,
Lives on credit till the fall;
And his pants are wearing thin, his condition it's a sin,
He's forgot that he's the man who feeds them all.
                                       chorus

                        —*Anonymous*

* THE MUSIC FOR THIS SONG IS TO BE FOUND IN *A Treasury of American Song* (SECOND EDITION, PAGE 292), EDITED BY OLIN DOWNES AND ELIE SIEGMEISTER, PUBLISHED BY ALFRED A. KNOPF, INC., NEW YORK.

Labor Is Not a Commodity

Like all social achievements, that of obtaining justice for the worker and enabling him to use his powers creatively for the good of all mankind needs the support of law, and we should familiarize ourselves with those great works of legislation which are the charter of economic democracy, no less than with those that are the charter of our political democracy.

Until very recent times, labor was considered a commodity, a piece of property that the worker bartered for his wage. Men forgot that a man's labor is part of his very self and that to treat it as a commodity is to condone his selling himself into bondage. Accordingly, ancient laws against conspiracy in restraint of trade were invoked to forbid labor to organize and strike for better conditions.

That shameful interpretation of the economic role of labor was corrected by the Norris-Clayton Act, approved October 16, 1904. Let us read some of the significant passages of that act.

THE LABOR OF A HUMAN BEING is not a commodity or article of commerce. Nothing contained in the anti-trust laws shall be construed to forbid the existence and operation of labor, agricultural, or horticultural organizations instituted for the purposes of mutual help and not having capital stock or conducted for profit, or to forbid or restrain individual members of such organizations from lawfully carrying out the legitimate objects thereof; nor shall such organizations, or the members thereof, be held or construed to be illegal combinations or conspiracies in restraint of trade under the anti-trust laws.

182

No restraining order or injunction shall be granted by any court of the United States . . . in any case between employers and employees . . . involving . . . a dispute concerning terms or conditions of employment, unless necessary to prevent irreparable injury to property, or to a property right of the party making the application, for which injury there is no adequate remedy at law. . . .

And no such restraining order or injunction shall prohibit any person or persons, whether singly or in concert, from terminating any relation of employment, or from ceasing to perform any work or labor, or from . . . persuading others by peaceful means to do so. . . .

How to Preserve the Dignity of Labor

THIS WORLD is the creation of God, and all men are the equal creatures of His bounty, the equal subjects of His providential care.

> All men are beset by the same physical wants, and the satisfaction of these wants depends on man's own exertions.

Thus has God given man the power, and laid on man the injunction, to labor.

> It is this power that raises him far above the brute, by making him a helper in the divine work of creation.

God has not put on man the task of making bricks without straw. With the need for labor and the power to labor he has also given to man the material for labor.

He has given man the land—and those other elements such as air, sunshine, and water, that man's possession of land puts at his disposal.

All men, being the equal creatures of the Creator, are equally entitled under His providence to live their lives and satisfy their needs.

All should have equal access to the land and its resources. To deny them this equal use of land is morally wrong.

And all men are entitled to the use of their own powers and the enjoyment of the fruits of their labor.

To deprive men of the products of their own toil is theft and a defiance of the law of God.

But the land belongs to God and its resources must be made available for the good of all God's children.

Its possession does not justify its exploitation for private gain; the withholding of its resources by private monopoly.

The worker is worthy of his hire and must not be asked to pay tribute to the greed of possessors who are not creators.

184

All benefit when labor is well rewarded, for the efficiency of labor is thereby enhanced.

Man is not a machine, that will do so much and no more; he is not an animal, whose powers may reach thus far and no further.

Give the worker his due and you will increase self-respect, intelligence, hope, and energy.

Mind, not muscle, is the great agent of production.

Man's physical power is one of the weakest of forces, but his mental power releases the resistless currents of nature, until matter becomes plastic to the human will.

To increase the comforts, and leisure, and independence of the masses is to increase their intelligence.

It brings the brain to the aid of the hand.

It engages in the common work of life the faculty which measures the animalcule and traces the orbit of the stars!

—Adapted from Henry George,
LETTER TO POPE LEO XIII, *and*
PROGRESS AND POVERTY

For a Land Without Masters and Without Slaves

What happens when the possession of the land and its resources is exploited for private greed and the worker is denied the just fruits of his labor is dramatically portrayed in the following eloquent appeal by Eugene V. Debs in behalf of the toilers in the mines under the conditions that prevailed in his day. The evils he describes have not yet been wholly removed. Listening to his plea should move us to support labor in its efforts to abolish the evils described.

TAKE THAT GREAT ARRAY OF WORKERS, called coal miners. . . . These miners are at the very foundation of industry and without their labor every wheel would cease to revolve as if by the decree of some industrial Jehovah. There are 600,000 of these slaves whose labor makes possible the firesides of the world, while their own loved ones shiver in the cold. . . . I have stood over these slaves and I have heard the echo of their picks, which sounded to me like muffled drums throbbing funeral marches to the grave, and I have said to myself . . . these wretches are simply following their own hearses to the potter's field. . . .

Then I have followed them from the depth of these black holes, over to the edge of the camp, not to the home, they have no home; but to a hut that is owned by the corporation that owns them, and here I have seen the wife—Victor Hugo once said that the wife of a slave is not a wife at all; she is simply a female that gives birth to young—I have seen this wife standing in the doorway, after trying all day long to make a ten-cent piece do the service of a half-dollar, and she was ill-humored; this could not be otherwise, for love and abject poverty do not dwell under the same roof . . . and in this atmosphere the children of the future are being reared. . . .

Man is the product, the expression of his environment. . . . The industrial soil and the social climate must be adapted to the development of men and women, and then society will cease producing the multiplied thousands of deformities that today are a rebuke to our vaunted civilization.

The workers are the saviors of society; the redeemers of the race; and when they have fulfilled their great historic mission, men and women can walk the highlands and enjoy the vision of a land without masters and without slaves, a land regenerated and resplendent in the triumph of Freedom and Civilization.

Prayers of Steel

In the short poem "Prayers of Steel," the poet Carl Sandburg voices symbolically the prayer of the worker, whether in steel or in any other substance, that his toil be not wasted, that it find a firm place, however humble, in the building of a heavenward-aspiring civilization. Let us read that prayer, making it our own.

Lay me on an anvil, O God.
Beat me and hammer me into a crowbar.

Let me pry loose old walls,
Let me lift and loosen old foundations.

Lay me on an anvil, O God
Beat me and hammer me into a steel spike.

Drive me into the girders that hold a sky-scraper
together
Take red-hot rivets and fasten me into the central
girders
Let me be the great nail holding a sky-scraper
through blue nights into white stars.

Solidarity *

When the union's inspiration through worker's blood
shall run,
There can be no power greater anywhere beneath the
sun;
Yet what force on earth is weaker than the feeble
strength of one,
For the union makes us strong.

CHORUS
Solidarity forever, Solidarity forever,
Solidarity forever, For the union makes us strong.

It is we who ploughed the prairies, built the cities
where they trade,

Dug the mines and built the workshops, endless miles
of railroad laid,
Now we stand outcast and starving 'mid the wonders
we have made,
But the union makes us strong.
CHORUS

They have taken untold millions that they never toiled
to earn,
But without our brain and muscle not a single wheel
can turn;
We can break their haughty power, gain our freedom
when we learn
That the union makes us strong.
CHORUS

In our hands is placed a power greater than their
hoarded gold,
Greater than the might of atoms magnified a thou-
sandfold;
We can bring to birth a new world from the ashes
of the old,
For the union makes us strong.
CHORUS

—*Ralph Chaplin*

* TO BE SUNG TO THE TUNE OF "*The Battle Hymn of the Republic.*"

Closing Prayer

THIS BLESSED LAND in which we dwell is rich in all the resources for satisfying human wants, and we, its people, have been amply endowed with the strength, knowledge, and art to convert these resources into the goods we need to live by. But without the further blessing of the spirit of justice, mutual loyalty, faith, and courage, we cannot build that civilization which would give evidence that we are created in God's image. Without this further blessing we cannot look upon our handiwork as a people and say, "Behold, it is very good." Humbly do we acknowledge that unless Thou, O God, build the house, they labor in vain that build it, that unless our work serve Thee and Thy kingdom of justice and peace, it cannot truly serve us, cannot help us to fulfill our manhood and womanhood and to find joy and happiness in our labor.

Give us, O God, the wisdom so to organize economic enterprise as to abolish all poverty, drudgery, and exploitation—all those social ills that are both effect and cause of man's inhumanity to man. Strengthen our faith in the promise of a better day for our people and for all peoples of the earth. Give us the courage to accept the hazards and endure the hardships which the creation of a free and cooperative society requires. Then shall we find joy in our labor and render eternal thanks to Thee for the privilege of sharing in Thy work of creation, O Thou who art the strength of our hands, the wisdom of our minds, and the spirit of love and loyalty in our hearts. AMEN.

SEPTEMBER 17

CONSTITUTION

DAY

A Day Devoted to the American Ideal
of a Government of Laws, Not of Men

The Significance of the Day

WE ARE MET TODAY to celebrate the anniversary of the signing of the Federal Constitution, to bring to mind what that sacred document has meant in the life of our people and of mankind. The Declaration of Independence asserts our will to freedom; the Constitution asserts our will to self-control. The former determined that we should not be subject to any foreign power; the latter that we should use our new-found freedom to establish justice and peace within our own borders.

The Constitution is not a perfect document. Its framers laid no claim to divine revelation. Realizing their own limitations, they provided that the generations who were to live by the Constitution should possess the right to amend it. But they were determined to produce a firm foundation in law for a free, just, and harmonious national life. And in this they succeeded.

They made our government one of laws and not of men, of laws designed to protect the rights of the weak against the encroachment of the strong, to defend the liberties of the individual not only against the tyranny of autocrats and privileged groups but also against the tyranny of the multitude. They wanted human law to reflect and enforce the divine law of justice and equity.

Well may we appeal on this day, in the words of the immortal Abraham Lincoln:

"Let reverence for the laws be breathed by every American mother to the lisping babe that prattles on her lap; let it be taught in schools, in seminaries, and in colleges; let it be written in primers, spelling-books, and in almanacs; let it be preached from the pulpit, proclaimed in legislative halls, and enforced in courts of justice. And, in short, let it become the political religion of the nation; and let the old and the young, the rich and the poor, the grave and the gay of all sexes and tongues and colors and conditions, sacrifice unceasingly upon its altars."

O Lord our God, may those inspired words strike a responsive chord in our hearts. May we ever be loyal to the principles of freedom and justice embodied in the law of our nation. May we have the wisdom to perfect the law where it needs improvement and to subject our personal and private aims to its benevolent authority. AMEN.

The American Hymn *

Speed our Republic, O Father on high!
Lead us in pathways of justice and right;
Rulers as well as the ruled, "One and all,"
Girdle with virtue the armor of might!
Hail! three times hail to our country and flag!
Rulers as well as the ruled, "One and all,"
Girdle with virtue the armor of might!
Hail! three times hail to our country and flag!

Rise up, proud eagle, rise up to the clouds,
Spread thy broad wings o'er this fair western world;
Fling from thy beak our dear banner of old—
Show that it still is for Freedom unfurl'd!
Hail! three times hail to our country and flag!
Fling from thy beak our dear banner of old—
Show that it still is for Freedom unfurl'd!
Hail! three times hail to our country and flag!

—*Mathias Keller*

* THE MUSIC FOR THIS SONG IS TO BE FOUND IN *Assembly Songs and Choruses* (PAGE 100), EDITED BY RANDALL J. CONDON, HELEN S. LEAVITT, AND ELBRIDGE W. NEWTON, PUBLISHED BY GINN AND COMPANY, BOSTON.

How to Use Our Constitution

THE CONSTITUTION is a great document, but greater than the Constitution itself is the principle of constitutionalism that it embodies,

> The principle that law must rule rather than brute force or arbitrary will.

If our law has perpetuated some abuses, it has also preserved all our liberties.

> The abuses are in no way essential to our law and can be eradicated, but, without the law, our liberties would be ours only on sufferance.

195

By constitutional means let us then guard our legal rights, while seeing to it that they shall never beget economic wrongs.

Let us strip of legal sanctions all existing wrongs and add the sanction of law to all reforms that our times require.

Let us strike at the corruption that is eating at the vitals of our body politic.

Let us invest our government with the power and the responsibility to resist the pressure of selfish interests and to advance the welfare of all the people.

May we so observe the letter and spirit of our Constitution that the humblest and even the most hated of our citizens will be secure in his person, his liberty, and his property.

May we indeed so revive and revise, clarify and extend the civil rights of our citizens as to give permanence to every achievement that leads to the goal of freedom, justice, and well-being for all our people.

—*Suggested by C. H. McIlwain,*
CONSTITUTIONALISM AND THE
CHANGING WORLD

The Constitution and the Federal Union

Never before the adoption of our Constitution was the principle of democracy applied to a vast territory with a population of many different racial and national origins. Could such a mixed multitude of people, living under different geographical conditions, with varying traditions and frequently conflicting economic interests, keep together as a self-governing nation? The Constitution was to be the instrument for effecting that union of free states. Without the Union, foreign powers that did not believe in self-government would soon have put an end to it on this continent. But our Constitution gave our people the vision of a great democratic Union that must never be dissolved.

It was the challenge to the Union from within that moved Abraham Lincoln to throw himself with all his might into the struggle to preserve the Union, and to subordinate all other issues, even that of the emancipation of the slaves, to that one crucial need. His faith in the Constitution as indispensable to the establishment of free government in the one part of the world where it had been attempted on so vast a scale is reflected in these, his words.

I WOULD SAVE THE UNION. I would save it the shortest way under the Constitution. The sooner the national authority can be restored, the nearer the Union will be "the Union as it was." If there be those who would not save the Union unless they could at the same time *destroy* Slavery, I do not agree with them. My paramount object in this struggle *is* to save the Union, and is *not* either to save or destroy Slavery.

If I could save the Union without freeing *any* slave, I would do it; and if I could save it by freeing *all* the slaves, I would do it; and if I could do it by freeing some and leaving others alone, I would also do that. What I do about Slavery and the colored race, I do because I believe it helps to save this Union; and what I forbear, I forbear because I do *not* believe it would help to save the Union. I shall do *less* whenever I shall believe what I am doing hurts the cause, and I shall do *more* whenever I shall believe doing more will help the cause. I shall try to correct errors when shown to be errors; and I shall adopt new views so fast as they shall appear to be true views. I have here stated my purpose according to my views of *official* duty, and I intend no modification of my oft-expressed *personal* wish, that all men, everywhere, could be free.

Union and Liberty Under Law

CIVILIZATION IS COOPERATION. Union and liberty are its factors.

> Whatever our civilization has achieved has been made possible by union and liberty under the sanction of law.

By binding themselves through law to respect one another's rights, men have set free the mental power which has rolled back the veil of ignorance;

That power which has measured the orbits of the circling spheres, has opened to us the antechamber of nature's mysteries, and has put at our disposal physical forces beside which man's efforts are puny.

The law of human progress, what is it but the moral law? When our laws promote justice, when they acknowledge the equality of right between man and man, when they insure to each the perfect liberty which is bounded only by the equal liberty of every other, then civilization advances.

And when our human laws fail to conform to the divine law of justice, when they enthrone special privilege and do not protect the citizen in his sacred right to life, liberty, and the pursuit of his happiness, civilization comes to a halt and recedes.

All religions at their best have ever striven for the rule of justice and mutual loyalty in the relations of men.

And all of modern scientific thinking about social and economic principles confirms the religious insight that only as men submit to the rule of justice and law can they achieve true freedom, peace, and well-being.

—Adapted from Henry George,
PROGRESS AND POVERTY

Abolitionist Hymn*

We ask not that the slave should lie
As lies his master, at his ease,
Beneath a silken canopy
Or in the shade of blooming trees.
We ask not "eye for eye," that all,
Who forge the chain and ply the whip,
Should feel their torture; while the thrall
Should wield the scourge of mastership.
We mourn not that the man should toil;
'Tis nature's need, 'tis God's decree;
But let the hand that tills the soil
Be, like the wind that fans it, free.

—*Anonymous*

*THE MUSIC FOR THIS SONG IS TO BE FOUND IN *A Treasury
of American Song* (SECOND EDITION, PAGE 68), EDITED BY OLIN
DOWNES AND ELIE SIEGMEISTER, PUBLISHED BY ALFRED A.
KNOPF, INC., NEW YORK.

The Purpose of the Federal Union and Its Authority

On this anniversary of the signing of the Constitution, it is fitting that we recite, in the language of that document, the purposes of our Federal Union and the scope of authority that, under the Constitution, has been delegated by the people of the United States to the Federal government.

All rise and recite in unison

WE THE PEOPLE of the United States, in order to form a more perfect union, establish justice, insure domestic tranquillity, provide for the common defense, promote the general welfare, and secure the blessings of liberty to ourselves and our posterity, do ordain and establish this constitution for the United States of America. . . .

This Constitution, and the laws of the United States which shall be made in pursuance thereof, and all treaties made, or which shall be made, under the authority of the United States shall be the supreme law of the land; and the judges in every state shall be bound thereby, anything in the Constitution or laws of any state to the contrary notwithstanding.

All are seated.

The Bill of Rights

The Constitution, as drafted by the Constitutional Convention, set up a complete frame of government for the Federal Union of the thirteen states that had come into existence when the thirteen British colonies in America declared their independence. But the people of the constituent states of the Union were not immediately prepared to accept the Constitution without reservations. They wanted guarantees against encroachments by the Federal government on the rights of the individual and of the states. For it was mainly such encroachments that had motivated their revolt against Great Britain. Various state conventions proposed amendments. It was only after certain of these amendments were accepted that the Constitution was finally ratified and went into effect. These first ten amendments of the Constitution, which are more in the nature of additions than of revisions, are known as the Bill of Rights. Let us read their principal provisions.

AMENDMENT I

Congress shall make no law respecting an establishment of religion, or prohibiting the free exercise thereof; or abridging the freedom of speech, or of the press, or the right of the people peaceably to assemble, and to petition the government for a redress of grievances.

AMENDMENT II

A well-regulated militia being necessary to the security of a free state, the right of the people to keep and bear arms shall not be infringed.

AMENDMENT III

No soldier shall in time of peace be quartered in any house without the consent of the owner, nor in time of war, but in a manner prescribed by law.

AMENDMENT IV

The right of the people to be secure in their persons, houses, papers, and effects, against unreasonable searches and seizures, shall not be violated. . . .

AMENDMENT V

No person shall be . . . deprived of life, liberty, or property without due process of law; nor shall private property be taken for public use, without just compensation.

AMENDMENT VI

In all criminal prosecutions, the accused shall enjoy the right to a speedy and public trial by an impartial jury . . . and to be informed of the nature and cause of the accusation; to be confronted with the witnesses against him; to have compulsory process for obtaining witnesses in his favor; and to have the assistance of counsel for his defense.

AMENDMENT VII

In suits at common law, where the value in controversy shall exceed twenty dollars, the right of trial by jury shall be preserved. . . .

AMENDMENT VIII

Excessive bail shall not be required, . . . nor cruel and unusual punishments inflicted.

AMENDMENT IX

The enumeration in the Constitution of certain rights shall not be construed to deny or disparage others retained by the people.

AMENDMENT X

The powers not delegated to the United States by the Constitution, nor prohibited by it to the States, are reserved to the States respectively, or to the people.

Who Made the Bill of Rights?

DO YOU THINK fifty-five representatives of the American people sat in a hall in New York City, in a drafty hall, and made up articles of freedom? Do you think the Congressmen from thirteen states made up those freedoms out of their own heads? Debated there, deliberated there, without assistance? Themselves? From their own experience? Ah, no. They had much help, from many nameless and unknown.

From dust in quiet places—from broken bones deep in the earth, deep in forgotten earth, mixed with empty clay.

From bleeding mouths, burnt flesh; chopped ears; from numberless and nameless agonies.

204

The delegates from dungeons, they were there.
The delegates from ashes at the bottom of the
stakes, they were there. . . .

The exiled wanderers; the Christians killed for being
Christians; Jews for being Jews; the Quakers hanged
in Boston town—they made a quorum also.

—*Adapted from Norman Corwin,*
WE HOLD THESE TRUTHS

A New Bill of Rights for Free Men

*The personal freedom to which in a democratic
society every individual is entitled involves the
possession of many rights in addition to those defined in our Constitution. The following are some
of the most important. They have been listed by
the National Resources Planning Board, and they
should be safeguarded by appropriate legislation
and administrative measures.*

1. The right to work usefully and creatively through
   the productive years.

2. The right to fair pay, adequate to command the
   necessities and amenities of life, in exchange for
   work, ideas, thrift.

3. The right to adequate food, clothing, shelter, and
   medical care.

4. The right to security, with freedom from fear of old age, want, dependency, sickness, and unemployment.

5. The right to live in a system of free enterprise.

6. The right to come and go, to speak or to be silent, free from spyings.

7. The right to equality before the law, with equal access to justice in fact.

8. The right to education, for work, for citizenship, and for personal growth.

9. The right to rest, recreation, and adventure; the opportunity to enjoy life.

Oh, Freedom *

Oh—freedom (freedom),
Oh—freedom (freedom),
Oh freedom over me (over me)
And before I'd be a slave,
I'll be buried in my grave,
And go home to my Lord and be free
        (and be free).

No more moaning
No more weeping
No more Jim-crow
There'll be singing.

And before I'll be a slave. I'll be buried
     in my grave;
Take my place with those who loved and
     fought before.

No more misery
No more starving
No more weeping
I know you're gonna miss me.

—Anonymous

* THE MUSIC FOR THIS SONG IS TO BE FOUND IN *The People's Song Book* (PAGE 21), EDITED BY WALDEMAR HILLE, PUBLISHED BY BONI & GAER, INC., NEW YORK.

The Essential Principles of Our Government

The Constitution and the Bill of Rights came into being only after much discussion and had their roots deep in the civilization that the early settlers in America brought with them from their native lands. Among the thinkers whose political philosophy deeply influenced the formulation of our basic law was Thomas Jefferson. He drafted the Declaration of Independence and later became the third president of the United States.

His inaugural address sums up what he regarded as "the essential principles of our government."

ABOUT TO ENTER, fellow-citizens, on the exercise of duties which comprehend everything dear and valuable to you, it is proper you should understand what I deem the essential principles of our Government, and consequently those which ought to shape its administration. I will compress them within the narrowest compass they will bear, stating the general principle, but not all its limitations. Equal and exact justice to all men, of whatever state or persuasion, religious or political; peace, commerce, and honest friendship with all nations, entangling alliances with none; the support of the State governments in all their rights, as the most competent administrations for our domestic concerns and the surest bulwarks against antirepublican tendencies; the preservation of the General Government in its whole constitutional vigor, as the sheet anchor of our peace at home and safety abroad; a jealous care of the right of election by the people—a mild and sage corrective of abuses which are lopped by the sword of revolution where peaceable remedies are unprovided; absolute acquiescence in the decisions of the majority, the vital principle of republics, from which is no appeal but to force, the vital principle and immediate parent of despotism; a well-disciplined militia, our best reliance in peace and for the first moments of war, till regulars may relieve them; the supremacy of the civil over the military authority; economy in the public expense, that labor may be lightly burthened; the honest payment of our debts and sacred preservation of the public faith; encouragement of agriculture, and commerce as its handmaid; the diffusion of information and arraignment of all abuses at the bar of the public reason; freedom of religion, freedom of the press, and freedom of person under the protection of the *habeas corpus,* and trial by juries impartially selected. These principles form the bright constellation which has gone before us and guided our steps through an age of revolution and reformation. The wisdom of our sages and blood of our heroes have been devoted to their attainment. They should be the creed of our political faith, the text of civic instruction, the touchstone by which to try the services of those we trust; and should we wander from them in moments of error or of alarm, let us hasten to retrace our steps and to regain the road which alone leads to peace, liberty, and safety.

The Principle of Equal Rights

Another of America's political philosophers who exerted a deep influence on the character of our Federal Constitution and the Bill of Rights was Thomas Paine. The following reading is adapted from one of his essays.

AN INQUIRY into the origin of rights will demonstrate to us that *rights* are not *gifts* from one man to another, nor from one class of men to another.

For who is he who could be the first giver; or by what principle, or on what authority, could he possess the right of giving?

A declaration of rights is not a creation of them, nor a donation of them; it is a manifest of the principle by which they exist, a statement of what the rights are.

Every civil right has a natural right for its foundation, and it includes the principle of a reciprocal guarantee of those rights from man to man.

Since there is no origin of rights otherwise than in the origin of man, all rights appertain to man in right of his existence only, and must therefore be equal to every man.

The principle of an *equality of rights* is clear; every man can understand it;

Every man must finally see the necessity of protecting the rights of others as the most effectual security for his own.

> But if we depart from the principle of equal rights, we plunge into a labyrinth of difficulties from which there is no way out but by retreating.

Where are we to stop? If property is to be made the criterion, it is a total departure from every moral principle of liberty.

> It is attaching rights to mere matter, and making man the agent of that matter.

It is holding up property as an apple of discord, and not only exciting but justifying war against it;

> When property is used as an instrument to take away the rights of those who do not possess property, it is used to an unlawful purpose, as firearms would be in a similar case.

All men are equal in rights, but they are not equal in power; the weak cannot protect themselves against the strong.

> The institution of civil society is for the purpose of making an equalization of powers that shall guarantee the equality of rights.

The laws of a country, when properly constructed, apply to this purpose; every man takes the arm of the law for his protection as more effectual than his own.

Therefore every man has an equal right in the formation of the government, and of the laws by which he is to be governed and judged.

God of Our Fathers *

God of our fathers, whose almighty hand
Leads forth in beauty all the starry band
Of shining worlds in splendor through the skies,
Our grateful songs before Thy throne arise.

Thy love divine hath led us in the past,
In this free land by Thee our lot is cast;
Be Thou our ruler, guardian, guide, and stay,
Thy word our law, Thy paths our chosen way.

Refresh Thy people on their toilsome way,
Lead us from night to never-ending day;
Fill all our lives with love and grace divine,
And glory, land, and praise be ever Thine.

—*Daniel C. Roberts*

* THE MUSIC FOR THIS SONG IS TO BE FOUND IN *Assembly Songs and Choruses* (PAGE 75), EDITED BY RANDALL J. CONDON, HELEN S. LEAVITT, AND ELBRIDGE W. NEWTON, PUBLISHED BY GINN AND COMPANY, BOSTON.

Ode

United States! the ages plead,—
    Present and Past in under-song,—
Go put your creed into your deed,
    Nor speak with double tongue.

For sea and land don't understand
    Nor skies without a frown
See rights for which the one hand fights
    By the other cloven down.

Be just at home; then write your scroll
    Of honor o'er the sea,
And bid the broad Atlantic roll
    A ferry of the free.

For he that worketh high and wise,
    Nor pauses in his plan,
Will take the sun out of the skies
    Ere freedom out of man.

—Ralph Waldo Emerson

The Universal Significance of Our Form of Government

Our Constitution was adopted for the government of our own country, but the principles of freedom and justice that it embodies are of universal significance. Those principles can be applied to the government of all other peoples who recognize their worth. And in our day, when a shrinking world has destroyed the isolation in which independent nations once lived, when we are beginning to lay the constitutional foundations of an international authority to establish and maintain the peace of the world, those principles need to be applied internationally as well as nationally.

One of the first to perceive this need was Woodrow Wilson. As our president during the First World War, he saw that the only thing that could save the world from chaos was a "universal dominion of right," by a concert of free peoples. In the message calling upon Congress to declare war against the German aggressor, he looked beyond the war toward a world, unified under the reign of law.

OUR OBJECT is to vindicate the principles of peace and justice as against selfish and autocratic power, and to set up among the really free and self-governed peoples of the world such a concert of purpose and of action as will henceforth insure the observance of those principles. . . .

We have no selfish ends to serve. We desire no conquest, no dominion. We seek no indemnities, no material compensation for the sacrifices we shall freely make. We are but one of the champions of the rights

214

of mankind. We shall be satisfied when those rights have been made as secure as the faith and the freedom of the nations can make them.

We shall fight for the things we have always carried nearest our hearts—for democracy, for the right of those who submit to authority to have a say in their own government, for the rights and liberties of small nations, for a universal dominion of right by such a concert of free peoples as shall bring peace and safety to all nations and make the world itself at last free.

Education in the Constitution

THE CONSTITUTION of the United States has been a great bulwark protecting the liberties of the American people.

Whenever these liberties were in danger of being overwhelmed by a tide of mass tyranny and state oppression, the Constitution served as a dike and averted the danger.

But it can serve that purpose only if we use it with wisdom and understanding; mere patriotic reverence of the Constitution is not enough.

Not even the memorizing of its every word will avail, for the mere words of the Constitution are not the law by which we live.

Words can be understood in so many different ways; the real Constitution is the interpretation put on these words by our courts as they grapple with the problems of our national life.

The principles of our law as laid down in the decisions of famous jurists need to be made the subject of reverent study.

High schools, colleges, and our whole citizenry should interest themselves continually in the application of Constitutional law to the issues of American life.

For only a people that knows its rights and its obligations can maintain its security and its freedom.

Ignorance of our rights invites their infringement, and neglect of our duties courts disaster.

Only that people is strong which knows its basic law and knows how to use it and, if need be, to amend it.

For no constitution is so perfect as never to need amendment. Even laws which, when enacted, serve good and useful ends may, under changed circumstances, work harm and defeat their original intent.

When any measure works evil instead of good, citizens have not only the right but also the duty to amend it.

For the Constitution was made for the people, not the people for the Constitution.

It is a marvelous instrument in our nation's possession; God grant us the knowledge and skill to use it for our welfare and the good of all mankind.

Closing Prayer

Our fathers' God! from out whose hand
The centuries fall like grains of sand,
We meet today, united, free,
And loyal to our land and Thee.
Here once of old, by Thy design,
The fathers spake that word of Thine
Whose echo is the glad refrain
Of rended bolt and falling chain.
Thou, who hast here in concord furled
The war flags of a gathered world,
Beneath our Western skies fulfill
The Orient's mission of good-will.
For art and labor met in truce,
For beauty made the bride of use,
We thank Thee; but, withal, we crave
The austere virtues strong to save,
The honor proof to place or gold,
The manhood never bought nor sold!
Oh make Thou us, through centuries long,

In peace secure, in justice strong;
Around our gift of freedom draw
The safeguards of Thy righteous law;
And cast in some diviner mould,
Let the new cycle shame the old!

—*Adapted from John Greenleaf Whittier,*
CENTENNIAL HYMN

COLUMBUS

DAY

A Day Devoted to an Appreciation
of the Exploring and Pioneering Spirit

The Significance of the Day

ON AUGUST 3RD, 1492, three small sailing ships under the command of Christopher Columbus set sail on a voyage fraught with more consequences than any other which history records. On October 12th, after almost six weeks of perilous adventure on the high seas, the vessels of Columbus at last reached land, a new land of whose existence even he had had no inkling. Thus was America discovered.

That is the event which we celebrate today and well may we do so. For Columbus to have undertaken that westward journey in the kind of ships available to men in those days was a great act of faith. The notion that the world was round and that one could reach the east by sailing toward the west had indeed been propounded before that time. The arguments were known to Columbus. But no one had yet put the theory to the test. How many well-reasoned theories have foundered on the rocks of hard fact! Columbus had the faith that the results of sound reason would be verified by experience. He had the courage to express his faith in action, in defiance of dangers both real and fancied.

And God blessed the faith of Columbus by rewarding it with a success beyond his dreams. His voyages uncovered a new continent in which the ancient civilizations of Europe could take root in virgin soil, renew their vigor, and yield a civilization such as the world had not yet known. That is what makes Columbus Day worthy of celebration.

It behooves us, the heirs of Columbus, to ask ourselves what use we have made of the opportunities that his discovery opened to mankind. Are the standards and ideals of our life here a mere replica of those by which our fathers lived in the old world? If so, Columbus dared and suffered in vain. Or have we here in America really discovered a new world, achieved a new way of life, developed a new type of civilization?

Let us set out today on a journey not unlike that of Columbus. Let us seek to rediscover America, to examine what the experience of the men who have taken up their home in this country has contributed and can continue to contribute to the welfare of mankind. And may God guide us in fulfilling the promise which the discovery of America by Columbus has held out to all humanity.

What America Makes of Men

WHAT THEN IS AN AMERICAN, this new man, shaped by the New World that Columbus discovered?

He is one who, leaving the prejudices and rancors of the Old World, embraces a new mode of life appropriate to the generosity of nature on this continent.

Here individuals of all nations are melted into a new community destined to cause great changes in the world.

Urged by a variety of motives they came here seeking a happier life, and everything has tended to regenerate them—new laws, a new mode of living, a new social system.

By what invisible power has this surprising transformation come about?

By the power of the laws and by the industry of the people.

The benign laws protect them as they arrive, and stamp on them the symbol of adoption.

Receiving ample rewards for their labors, they win the title of freemen and to that title every benefit is affixed which man can want.

The American must love this country, where the rewards of his industry follow with equal steps the progress of his labor.

In this new world the American is a new man, entertaining new ideas, forming new opinions, acting on new principles.

Released by the lavishness of nature and the justice of the laws from involuntary idleness, servile dependence, and penury, the American can devote his labor to creative tasks.

Grateful to God for his blessings, he is moved
to share them with his fellow men and to seek
the freedom and well-being of all humanity.

—*Adapted from Jean de Crevecoeur,*
LETTER FROM AN AMERICAN FARMER

America Triumphant *

America triumphant!
Brave land of pioneers!
On mountain peak and prairie
Their winding trail appears.
The wilderness is planted;
The deserts bloom and sing;
On coast and plain the cities
Their smoky banners fling.

America triumphant!
Dear homeland of the free!
Thy sons have fought and fallen,
To win release for thee.
They broke the chains of empire;
They smote the wrongs of state;
And lies of law and custom
They blasted with their hate.

America, America!
Triumphant thou shalt be!
Thy hills and vales shall echo
The shouts of liberty.

224

Thy bards shall sing thy glory,
Thy prophets tell thy praise,
And all thy sons and daughters
Acclaim thy golden days. Amen.

—*John Haynes Holmes*

* THE MUSIC FOR THIS SONG IS TO BE FOUND IN *Hymns for the Living Age* (PAGE 406), EDITED BY H. AUGUSTINE SMITH, PUBLISHED BY THE FLEMING H. REVELL COMPANY, NEW YORK.

America the Country of the Future

WE CANNOT LOOK on the freedom of this country without a presentiment that here shall laws and institutions exist on some scale of proportion to the majesty of nature.

To men legislating for the area betwixt the two oceans, betwixt the snows and the tropics, somewhat of the gravity of nature will infuse itself into the code.

A mixed multitude, crowding on all ships from all corners of the world to the ports of America, and thence proceeding inward to the prairie and the mountains, quickly contribute their private thought to the public opinion, their toll to the treasury, and their vote to the election.

225

It cannot be doubted that the legislation of such a country should become more universal and cosmopolitan than that of any other.

It should be easy for America to inspire and express the most expansive and humane spirit.

New-born, free, healthful, strong, the land of the laborer, of the democrat, of the philanthropist, of the believer, of the saint, America should speak for the human race.

America is the country of the Future; through all its cities, states, and territories, it is a country of beginnings, of projects, of designs, of expectations.

Here is manifest a sublime and friendly Destiny by which the human race is guided, and though men be narrow and selfish, that Destiny is not narrow but beneficent.

Here in America is the home of man; here the human mind is offered an opportunity not known in any other region.

After all the deduction is made for our frivolities and insanities, there still remains in America an organic simplicity and liberty.

Compared to the venerable antiquities of Europe, our houses and towns are like mosses and lichens, so slight and new.

But youth is a fault which we shall daily mend.

This land, too, is as old as the Flood, and wants no ornament or privilege which nature could bestow.

Here stars, woods, hills, animals, men abound, and the vast tendencies concur of a new order.

If only our people act in harmony with the designs of the Spirit who led us hither and is leading us still, we shall quickly enough advance out of all hearing of others' censures.

And with no regrets of our own, we shall achieve a new and more excellent social state than history has yet recorded.

—*Adapted from Ralph Waldo Emerson,*
THE YOUNG AMERICAN

Prayer for God's Guidance
in Our Explorations

Would that we had the fortunes of Columbus,
Sailing his caravels a trackless way,
He found a universe—he sought Cathay.
God give such dawns as when, his venture o'er,
The Sailor looked upon San Salvador.
God lead us past the setting of the sun
To wizard islands, of august surprise;
God make our blunders wise.

—*Vachel Lindsay,*
LITANY OF THE HEROES

The Discovery of America as Columbus Described It

It is appropriate on Columbus Day that we seek inspiration by recalling in imagination that thrilling moment when, after weary weeks of hardship and peril, the new world—or, as Columbus thought, the newly discovered, very old world of Asia—loomed in sight. Let us read of the events of that day as Columbus himself recorded them in the journal that he kept of his voyages. He writes of himself in the third person as "the admiral."

Wednesday, 10 October

. . . Here the men could now bear no more; they complained of the long voyage. But the admiral heartened them as best he could, holding out to them bright hopes of the gains which they could make, and he added that it was vain to complain, since he was going to the Indies and that so he must pursue his course until, with the help of Our Lord, he found them.

Thursday, 11 October

He navigated to the west-south-west; they had a rougher sea than they had experienced during the whole voyage. They saw sandpipers and a green branch near the ship. Those in the caravel *Pinta* saw a cane and a stick, and they secured another small stick, carved, as it appeared, with iron, and a piece of cane, and other vegetation which grows on land, and a small branch. Those in the caravel *Nina* also saw other indications of land and a small branch covered with dog-roses. At these signs all breathed again and rejoiced. . . . After sunset he steered his former course to the west. . . . And since the caravel *Pinta* was swifter and went ahead of the admiral, she found land and made the signals which the admiral had commanded. This land a sailor who was called Rodrigo de Triana first sighted, although the admiral at ten o'clock in the night, being on the castle of the poop, saw a light. It was, however, so obscure that he would not affirm that it was land, but called Pero Gutierrez, a gentleman of the bedchamber to the king, and told him that there seemed to be a light, and that he should watch for it. He did so and saw it. He said the same also to Rodrigo Sanchez de Segovia . . . and he saw nothing, since he was not in a position from which it could be seen. After the admiral had so spoken, it was seen two or three times, and it was like a small wax candle, which was raised and lowered. Few thought that this was an indication of land, but the admiral was certain that it was on land. Accordingly, when they had said the *Salve,* which all the sailors are accustomed to say and to chant in their manner . . . the admiral asked and urged them to keep a good look out from the forecastle and to watch carefully for land, and to him who should say first that he saw land, he would give at once a silk doublet, apart from the other rewards which the sovereigns had promised. . . . Two hours after midnight, land appeared at a distance of two leagues from them. They shortened all sail . . . and lay to, waiting for day, a Friday, on which they reached a small island of the Lucayos, which is called in the language of the Indians "Guanahani." Immediately they saw naked people, and the admiral went ashore in the armed boat, and Martin Alonso Pinzon and Vincente Yanez, his brother, who was captain of the *Nina*. The admiral brought out the royal standard and the captains went with two banners of the green cross, which the admiral flew on all ships as a flag, with an F and a Y, and over each letter their crown, one being on one side of the cross and the other on the other. . . . The admiral called the two captains and the others who had landed, and Rodrigo de Escobedo, secretary of the whole fleet, and Rodrigo Sanchez de Segovia and said that they should bear witness and testimony how he, before them all, took possession, as in fact he took, of the said island for the king and queen, his sovereigns, making the declarations which are required, as is contained more at length in the testimonies which were there made in writing.

The Prayer of Columbus

*Columbus had his brief days of triumph, but
then he had to endure the tragedy of many great
men who suffer ingratitude in their lifetime and
are appreciated only after their death. Ignominy
and grief befell Columbus. The imagination of
Walt Whitman seized on the tragic circumstances
of Columbus' end as material for a noble poem in
the form of a soliloquy. In the following prayer,
we read the poet's interpretation of the significance
of the life and work of the discoverer of America.*

A batter'd old man,
Thrown on this savage shore, far, far from home,
Pent by the sea, and dark rebellious brows, twelve
      dreary months,
Sore, stiff with many toils, sickened, and nigh to death,
I take my way along the island's edge,
Venting a heavy heart.

I am too full of woe!
Haply, I may not live another day;
I cannot rest, O God—I cannot eat or drink or sleep,
Till I put forth myself, my prayer, once more to Thee,
Breathe, bathe myself once more in Thee—commune
      with Thee,
Report myself once more to Thee.

Thou knowest my years, entire, my life,
(My long and crowded life of active work—not
      adoration merely:)

All my emprises have been filled with Thee
My speculations, plans, begun and carried on in
      thoughts of Thee,

Sailing the deep, or journeying the land for Thee;
Intuitions, purports, aspirations mine—leaving my
        results to Thee.
O I am sure they really come from Thee!
The urge, the ardor, the unconquerable will,
The potent, felt, interior command stronger than
        words,
A message from the Heavens, whispering to me even
        in sleep,
These sped me on.

By me, and these, the work so far accomplished
        (for what has been, has been),
By me Earth's elder, cloy'd and stifled lands, uncloy'd,
        unloos'd;
By me the hemisphere rounded and tied—the un-
        known to the known.
The end I know not—it is all in Thee.

My terminus near,
The clouds already closing in upon me,
The voyage balked—the course disputed, lost,
I yield my ships to Thee.
Steersman unseen! henceforth the helms are Thine;
Take Thou command—(what to my petty skill Thy
        navigation?)

My hands, my limbs grow nerveless;
My brain feels rack'd, bewilder'd;
Let the old timbers part—I will not part!
I will cling fast to Thee, O God, though the waves
        buffet me;
Thee, Thee, at last I know.

Is it the prophet's thought I speak, or am I raving?
What do I know of life? what of myself?
I know not even my own work, past or present;
Dim, ever-shifting guesses of it spread before me,
Of newer better worlds, their mighty parturition,
Mocking, perplexing me.

And these things I see suddenly—what mean they?
As if some miracle, some hand divine unseals my eyes,
Shadowy, vast shapes smile through the air and sky,
And on the distant waves sail countless ships,
And anthems in new tongues I hear saluting me.

Boston Hymn

*The era of discovery initiated by Columbus was
followed by the era of exploration and settlement.
The discovery of the land made possible the discovery of a new way of living in the land, which
we call by the name of Americanism. Among the
settlers who contributed much to that way of life
were the Puritans who settled in Massachusetts.
The following poem recalls the spirit of their settlement and its significance, as seen by one of their
descendants, Ralph Waldo Emerson.*

The word of the Lord by night
To the watching Pilgrims came,
As they sat by the seaside,
And filled their hearts with flame.

God said, I am tired of kings,
And I suffer them no more;
Up to my ear the morning brings
The outrage of the poor.

Lo! I uncover the land,
Which I hid of old time in the West,
As the sculptor uncovers the statue
When he has wrought his best;

I show Columbia, of the rocks
Which dip their foot in the seas,
And soar to the air-borne flocks
Of clouds and the boreal fleece.

I will divide my goods;
Call in the wretch and slave;
None shall rule but the humble,
And none but Toil shall have.

I will have never a noble,
No lineage counted great;
Fishers and choppers and ploughmen
Shall constitute a state.

Go, cut down trees in the forest
And trim the straightest boughs;
Cut down trees in the forest
And build me a wooden house.

Call the people together,
The young men and the sires,
The digger in the harvest-field,
Hireling and him that hires;

And here in a pine state-house
They shall choose men to rule
In every needful faculty,
In church and state and school.

Lo, now! if these poor men
Can govern the land and sea,
And make just laws below the sun,
As planets faithful be.

And ye shall succor men;
'Tis nobleness to serve;
Help them who cannot help again:
Beware from right to swerve.

I break your bonds and masterships,
And I unchain the slave;
Free be his heart and hand henceforth
As wind and wandering wave.

I cause from every creature
His proper good to flow;
As much as he is and doeth,
So much he shall bestow.

Come, East and West and North,
By races, as snowflakes,
And carry my purpose forth,
Which neither halts nor shakes.

The Breaking Waves Dashed High *

The breaking waves dashed high
On a stern and rock-bound coast,
And the woods against a stormy sky
Their giant branches tossed,
And the heavy night hung dark
The hills and waters o'er
When a band of exiles moored their bark
On the wild New England shore.

Not as the conq'ror comes,
They, the true-hearted came;
Not with the roll of stirring drums
And the trumpet that sings of fame;
Not as the flying come
In silence and in fear,
They shook the depths of the desert gloom
With their hymns of lofty cheer.

Amidst the storm they sang,
And the stars heard, and the sea;
And the sounding aisles of the dim woods rang
With the anthem of the free.
The ocean eagle soared
From his nest by the white waves' foam,
And the rocking pines of the forest roar'd;
This was their welcome home.

What sought they thus afar?
Bright jewels from the mine?
The wealth of seas, the spoils of war?
They sought a faith's pure shrine,

Ay, call it holy ground,
The soil where first they trod,
They have left unstained what there they found,
Freedom to worship God.

—*Felicia D. Hemans*

* THE MUSIC FOR THIS SONG IS TO BE FOUND IN *Assembly Songs and Choruses* (PAGE 142), EDITED BY RANDALL J. CONDON, HELEN S. LEAVITT, AND ELBRIDGE W. NEWTON, PUBLISHED BY GINN AND COMPANY, BOSTON.

The Character of the American Backwoodsman

From the fringe of settlements on the coastal plains, which is all that there was of the United States when its independence was won, bold pioneers set out to explore the continent and to blaze a way for the civilization that was to follow. The hardships they endured, their isolation, and their insecurity, developed in them traits of character and attitudes of mind that have become part of the American tradition. It is interesting to see how the American backwoodsmen impressed a cultured man at the end of the eighteenth century who passed some time among them. This is what Timothy Flint, writing in 1798, had to say about them.

. . . THE BACKWOODSMAN OF THE WEST, as I have seen him, is generally an amiable and virtuous man. His general motive for coming here is to be a freeholder, to have plenty of rich land, and to be able to settle his children about him. It is a most virtuous motive. And notwithstanding all that Dr. Dwight and Talleyrand have said to the contrary, I fully believe that nine in ten of the emigrants have come here with no other motive. You find, in truth, that he has vices and barbarisms, peculiar to his situation. His manners are rough. He wears, it may be, a long beard. He has a great quantity of bear or deer skins wrought into his household establishment, his furniture, and dress.

He carries a knife, or a dirk in his bosom, and when in the woods has a rifle on his back, and a pack of dogs at his heels. An Atlantic stranger, transferred directly from one of our cities to his door, would recoil from an encounter with him. But remember that his rifle and his dogs are among his chief means of support and profit. Remember that all his first days here were passed in dread of the savages. Remember that he still encounters them, still meets bears and panthers.

Enter his door, and tell him you are benighted, and wish the shelter of his cabin for the night. The welcome is indeed seemingly ungracious: "I reckon you can stay," or "I suppose we must let you stay." But this apparent ungraciousness is the harbinger of every kindness that he can bestow, and every comfort that his cabin can afford. Good coffee, corn bread and butter, venison, pork, wild and tame fowls are set before you. His wife, timid, silent, reserved, but constantly attentive to your comfort, does not sit at the table with you, but like the wives of the patriarchs stands and attends on you. You are shown to the best bed which the house can offer. When this kind of hospitality has been afforded, you stay as long as you choose to stay, and when you depart, and speak about your bill, you are most commonly told with some slight mark of resentment, that they do not keep tavern. Even the flaxen-headed urchins will turn away from your money.

. . . For myself, the western country is endeared to me by a thousand recollections. Its beautiful scenery has left traces in my memory which will never be effaced. The hospitality of its inhabitants to me, and to those who are most dear to me, has marked on my heart deep impressions of gratitude. I hail the anticipation that in a century to come it will be a great and populous country, as great in a moral point of view as it is at present rich in natural resource and beauty.

Pioneers! O Pioneers!

To be read by the leader, the entire assembly joining in the refrain of each stanza—"Pioneers! O Pioneers!"

Come my tan-faced children,
Follow well in order, get your weapons ready,
Have you your pistols? Have you your sharp-edged
      axes?
Pioneers! O Pioneers!

For we cannot tarry here,
We must march my darlings, we must bear the brunt
      of danger,

We the youthful sinewy races, all the rest on us
    depend.
    Pioneers! O Pioneers!

O you youths, Western youths,
So impatient, full of action, full of manly pride and
    friendship,
Plain I see you, Western youths, see you tramping with
    the foremost,
    Pioneers! O Pioneers!

O resistless, restless race!
O beloved race in all! O my breast aches with tender
    love for all!
O I mourn and yet exult, I am rapt with love for all,
    Pioneers! O Pioneers!

Do the feasters gluttonous feast?
Do the corpulent sleepers sleep? have they locks and
    bolted doors?
Still be ours the diet hard, and the blanket on the
    ground,
    Pioneers! O Pioneers!

Has the night descended?
Was the road of late so toilsome? did we stop
    discouraged nodding on our way?
Yet a passing hour I yield you in your tracks to pause
    oblivious,
    Pioneers! O Pioneers!

Till with sound of trumpet,
Far, far off the daybreak call—hark! how loud and
    clear I hear it wind,

Swift! to the head of the army!—swift! spring to
    your places,
    Pioneers! O Pioneers!

—*Walt Whitman*

America—Land of Opportunity

AMERICA IS NOT PERFECT. That we know. But
it is ours, and it has been for a century the dream of
freedom of every European. We must keep it so.

Its streets have never been paved with gold, and
they never will be, but America should ever stand
as a land of opportunity and enthusiasm and
riches.

The riches that we prize are not only raw materials,
armies, navies, railroads, ships, and cities, but a whole
people full of good will towards the world, loyal to its
own flag and beautiful continent.

Our whole people must educate itself for its task
of helping all mankind to the benefits of democracy.

We must look over the whole world to find allies in
building a world of equal opportunity for all classes
and all races.

241

But we cannot establish democracy in far places, if in our own house, own schools, own factories and shops, in our own country and city, our conduct does not square with the slogans and spirit of our democracy.

Let it be our daily practice to help one another and let us keep our eyes open to know and guard not only our own advantage but the common interests of mankind in justice and peace.

Grateful to God for our blessings, let us hold fast to our ideals.

Let us lift up our eyes to the hills of vision, for "Where there is no vision, the people perish."

—*Adapted from Mrs. J. Borden Harriman*, WHAT AMERICA EXPECTS OF ITS YOUTH

Unmanifest Destiny

To what new fates, my country, far
    And unforeseen of foe or friend,
Beneath what unexpected star
    Compelled to what unchosen end,

Across the sea that knows no beach,
    The Admiral of Nations guides

Thy blind obedient keels to reach
    The harbor where thy future rides!

There is a Hand that bends our deeds
    To mightier issues than we planned:
Each son that triumphs, each that bleeds,
    My country, serves its dark command.

I do not know beneath what sky
    Nor on what seas shall be thy fate:
I only know it shall be high,
    I only know it shall be great.

                    —*Richard Hovey*

America

My country! 'tis of thee,
Sweet land of liberty,
    Of thee I sing;
Land where my fathers died!
Land of the Pilgrims' pride!
From ev'ry mountain side
    Let freedom ring.

My native country, thee,
Land of the noble free—
    Thy name I love;
I love thy rocks and rills,

Thy woods and templed hills,
My heart with rapture thrills
Like that above.

Let music swell the breeze,
And ring from all the trees
Sweet freedom's song:
Let mortal tongues awake,
Let all that breathe partake,
Let rocks their silence break,
The sound prolong.

Our fathers' God to Thee
Author of liberty,
To Thee we sing;
Long may our land be bright
With freedom's holy light!
Protect us by thy might,
Great God our King!

Samuel Francis Smith

Closing Prayer

LORD OF THE UNIVERSE, Thou hast endowed
man with the spirit of curiosity and adventure, to settle remote regions of the world, to subdue the asperi-
ties of nature and make it yield the fulfillment of his
wants. Under Thy guidance men have learned the arts
of civilization, which, if used in conformity with Thy

just and holy will, are an unfailing source of salvation and blessing.

In every generation, Thou revealest to men new vistas of achievement and sendest them in quest of new and distant goals. The full meaning of their quest they as little know as Columbus could know the tremendous consequences of his bold enterprise. But Thy wisdom gives to every human undertaking its full and final meaning.

We therefore beseech Thee, O God, as once Thou didst guide the caravels of Columbus, guide Thou our ship of state. Save it from all perilous seas that would engulf it. Inspire its crew with courage, wisdom, and steadfastness of purpose. Far horizons beckon us to a new and better world than any mankind has yet known, a world of freedom and justice, of truth and honesty, of friendship, loyalty, and peace. Thou hast sent us on this quest. Be Thou our Pilot. AMEN.

OCTOBER 24

UNITED NATIONS

DAY

A Day Devoted to the **Ideal of**
World Peace and World **Unity**

The Significance of the Day

WE ARE ASSEMBLED to celebrate the anniversary of the day in the year 1945 when the Charter of the United Nations went into effect. With the adoption of that Charter, the first step was taken toward bringing all the nations of the world into a law-bound convenant to respect one another's rights.

What is a nation? It is people who live in a land of their own, who live in it and derive their living from it; people bound together by common memories, by shared experiences, and by the ideals and aspirations that have grown out of those experiences.

Each nation thus possesses a character of its own. The national character helps mold the life of every man and woman in the nation and every man and woman adds something of his own to the life of the nation. No person is merely an individual. His very personality is rooted in the soil of his nation, reflects its landscape, thinks in its language, responds to its moral standards, laws, and customs. In the permanence of the nation his own life acquires abiding meaning; the resources of the nation enhance his meager powers; the security of the nation protects his own. The sovereignty of the nation derives from the nation's need to be free to help its people obtain these blessings. Each nation should therefore be allowed to live its own life, to seek its own welfare, and to make its own contribution to civilization.

But national sovereignty must not be absolute. It must always be subject to the sovereignty of God, to whom belongs the earth and the fullness thereof. It must conform to His law of justice. When nations act arbitrarily in their own interest and disregard the needs and the rights of other nations, they usurp God's sovereignty and render idolatrous obeisance to their own national ego. Nationalism then turns from a blessing to a curse. This has been the tragedy of human history with its record of recurrent wars that wreak havoc with human lives.

Aggressive nationalism has been the scourge of mankind in every age, but in ours it menaces the very existence of the race of man. Technology has shrunk the dimensions of our world and bound together in one economic mesh people of all races and all climes. We are all neighbors now and must learn to live together as neighbors. International war is an anachronism that must be abolished. Wars have become too destructive to be tolerated. Their devastation affects the lives not only of the participants but of whole populations, including millions of people who have no share in waging them. War has become mutual genocide. There is no victory in modern war, save for the vulture, the worm, and the disease germ.

Under such conditions national sovereignty can no longer mean complete national independence; it must mean the equality of interdependent nations. It calls for the union of all nations, great and small, to protect the rights of each and advance the good of all.

Let us look upon mankind's plight as a challenge from God, who tells us: "I have set before you life and death, the blessing and the curse. Choose, therefore, life." The decision of the nations to unite was a choice of life. If the nations will be loyal to the United Nations charter, mankind will live.

Rededication for America

WE AMERICANS are heirs to a rich estate. We deemed it ours alone when other peoples lived far beyond our ken.

> But now they live at our door; their cries of pain and want give us no rest.

In a world that is one, there is but one fate for all men.

> Though a nation's bounds may keep out the victims of war; none can keep out its hatreds and miseries; none can prevent it from setting all the world aflame.

Once we looked Westward and inward for the American future; hereafter, we must look all about us.

> For we are members of one global family and share the lot of every clime and people.

Once we thought our unstable horizon would stiffen into fixity.

> Now we behold it expanding till it includes all the world within its limits.

Be it, therefore, our ambition to bring peace to this racked, agonized, exhausted planet.

> To set up a world order that shall promote justice and progress.

Let us make of the sense of comradeship which we seek to foster among the many races and creeds that inhabit our land the bond to unite all nations.

Let all the world heed the law of God that decrees that the many shall be one.

With the call of universal distress in our ears we cannot have our Ship of State rest idle in port and refuse to brave the tempest in order to bring other craft to a safe haven.

Forget not, O America, that
"Humanity with all its fears,
With all its hopes of future years,
Is hanging breathless on thy fate."

—Adapted from Allan Nevins

United Nations*

United Nations make a chain,
Ev'ry link is freedom's name,
Keep your hand on that plow, hold on.

CHORUS
Hold on, hold on.
Keep your hand on that plow, hold on.

Now the war is over and done,
Let's keep the peace that we have won;
Keep your hand on that plow, hold on!
CHORUS

Freedom's name is mighty sweet;
Black and white are gonna meet;
Keep your hand on that plow, hold on!
CHORUS

Many men have fought and died
So we could be here side by side;
Keep your hand on that plow, hold on!
CHORUS

—*Anonymous*

* THE MUSIC FOR THIS SONG IS TO BE FOUND IN *The People's Song Book* (PAGE 59), EDITED BY WALDEMAR HILLE, PUBLISHED BY BONI & GAER, INC., NEW YORK.

Create Great Peace

Would you end war?
Create great Peace . . .
The Peace that demands all of a man,
His love, his life, his veriest self;
Plunge him into the smelting fires of a work that
        becomes his child . . .

Give him a hard Peace; a Peace of discipline and
        justice . . .
Kindle him with vision, invite him to joy and
        adventure:
Set him to work, not to create *things*
But to create *man:*
Yea, himself.

Go search your heart, America . . .
Turn from the machine to man,
Build, while there is yet time, a creative Peace . . .
While there is yet time! . . .
For if you reject great Peace,
As surely as vile living brings disease,
So surely will your selfishness bring war.

        —*Adapted from James Oppenheim,*
        1914—AND AFTER

Thus Saith The Lord

*The following is an excerpt from a longer com-
position which appeared in a religious magazine
under the title "Amos on Times Square." It was
introduced by a statement declaring it to be "The
words of Amos, a farmer of Pleasantville, which
he saw concerning the nation, and which he spoke
to the crowds on Times Square, two weeks after
the bombing of Pearl Harbor, in the days of
Franklin Roosevelt and Adolf Hitler." The com-
position paraphrases passages from the prophecies
contained in the book of Amos and shows how
their thought is related to the problems that con-
front us today. The passage we have excerpted is
particularly applicable to the relationship of America to the United Nations.*

THUS SAITH THE LORD:

Think not, O people of America, that ye are the
chosen of the earth, inasmuch as I have cast your lives
in pleasant places, and given you the kidney fat of
wheat and the rich corn, and have made you the millers and meat-packers for the world. Think not that
ye are set above my other children. For your people
are but branches of my planting in lands across the
seas. Ye are a nation of nations—in you is all of Europe and Asia and Africa. Think not that the cushions
of water about your lands are shields from the pestilence that walketh by day, or the arrow that flieth by
night.

Egypt was mighty in its day, and Babylon no less.
Assyria called itself "Invincible Eagle," and Rome
anointed herself "Mistress of all Lands and all Seas."
Yet, I destroyed these mighty Empires, their fruit
from above, and their roots from beneath. Their

names are but faded echoes in the ear of Time, and their vauntings, the babbling of children.

People of America, take this to heart and consider it well. Ye have I endowed more richly than all other nations. Ye have I given soil veined with silver beneath and crowned with fields of golden grain. Ye have I given forests of good wood, and lakes and rivers abounding in fish. And I have brought you tested men to match my mountains. Therefore, do I expect of you a double responsibility, and will visit upon you all your iniquities.

For, have ye not heard that the Earth is mine, and all that is therein? Hath it not been proclaimed aforetime that the Lord God is Father to all; that the children of Manchuria, Ethiopia and Andalusia are as dear unto me as the children of England and America: Wherefore, then, didst thou smugly wrap thy oceans about thee and turn thy broad back on Europe's woes, that time my servant Woodrow Wilson pleaded that ye rise to your high-born part and create a League of Nations, in the image of the United States? Where was thy brotherly heart when the Chinese perished, and the Ethiopians were murdered and the Spanish massacred by the unrepentant sons of Edom, the streamlined barbarians of earth? Did you not say, as Cain of old: "Am I my brother's keeper?" Two mighty oceans of water will not dilute the brother blood in the heart of my creatures. Therefore, the very ground cries out with the blood of the innocent, and will not open itself to thee until every drop of blood drawn from my abandoned children is recompensed by one drawn from those who were callous of heart. It will go ill with thee, but by Justice, and Justice alone, can the Earth endure.

The voice of sorrow will be heard in the land
As the mourning for an only son,
And the end thereof as a bitter day.
Thus shall all the stored-up violence be expressed
And the ancient wrongs be requited in blood.

Then will the remnant of the people be sound,
And get them a heart of wisdom at last,
And raise up a permanent Assembly for all
    nations;
A Court of Justice for all peoples.
And Peace, girdered by Justice, shall come back
    to earth,
And men will turn their swords into plow-shares,
And breathe freedom from the four winds,
With none to make them afraid.

Behold, the abundant days come,
That the plowman shall overtake the reaper,
And the treader of grapes, him that soweth seed;
And I will restore the captive peoples to their
    lands.
And men shall build the waste cities and inhabit
    them;
They shall make gardens, and eat the fruit of
    them.
And Man shall no more be plucked up out of the
    land which is his home.
On that day alone shall man inherit the earth,
And be worthy of his God.

                              —*Jacob J. Weinstein*

What America Shall Strive For

LET AMERICA BE FIRST not merely in matters material, but in things of the spirit;

> Not merely in science, inventions, motors, and skyscrapers, but also in ideals, principles, character;

Not merely in the calm assertion of rights, but in the glad assumption of duties.

> Let her not flaunt her strength as a giant, but bend it in helpfulness over a sick and wounded world like a Good Samaritan.

Let her live not in splendid isolation, but in courageous cooperation.

> Not in pride, arrogance, and disdain of other races and peoples, but in sympathy, love, and understanding.

Not in treading again the old, worn, bloody pathway which ends inevitably in chaos and disaster, but in blazing new trails, along which, please God, other nations will follow, into the new Jerusalem where wars shall be no more.

> Some day some nation must take that path, and that honor we covet for our beloved America.

And so, in that spirit and with these hopes, we say with all our heart and soul, "America First."

—Adapted from G. Ashton Oldham

The Carnival Is Over

Behold,
The Carnival is over
The reveling and feasting
Is done!
The vineyards burned,
The fleshpots empty!
And all the plains of ease,
And all the pools of safety
Dried up, scorched!
The Age of Godlessness
Is ended.
Wasted like a Sun.

Beneath
The gaunt and gaping roofs,
Its multi-colored gauds of lust,
Like bits of stained confetti,
Lie dispersed and scattered
In the dust.
The ample couches,
Jeweled thrones,
The palaces
And perilous dreams,
All,
All have been laid waste
Forever

Beneath the Night's
Uprooted beams.

The Age of Godlessness
Is ended!
Blasted,
Burned,
And spent.
Its heathen gods,
Its brazen altars,
And all its citadels
Built with blood,
And all its fortresses
Bought with iniquity—
Are come to naught,
Are mounds of reeking clay.
And North and South,
And East and West,
Its bastions are crumbling,
And all its buttresses
Are mouldering away.

Though here and there
Amidst the ruins,
Like jackals
In a wilderness
At night,
Some risen clown
Or fallen king

Still spouts with violence,
Still issues out
A travesty of Justice,
A farce of Truth,
And everlasting Right.
Such crying is
As of the grave—
Even now
Degenerous with decay—
And nevermore
Shall it obstruct
The light,
The Dawning Light
Of a merciful
New Day!

Ye poor and needy
Of all nations,
Ye tricked and taunted
Of the earth,
Behold,
Beyond the ruthless carnage,
Beyond the spoil
And the rage—
Your Blood has stormed
The Gates of Heaven,
And brings to birth
The Promised Age!

—*Silvia Margolis*

261

War *Can* Be Abolished

THROUGH ALL the recorded history of man, there have been wars. Man seems to be a belligerent animal. Must one then accept the dismal forecasts of those who say wars are necessary and inevitable?

> The protest of the human spirit against such a destiny for mankind, its detestation of the waste and carnage of war, its recognition of the disastrous consequences for the victors as well as for the vanquished—these give us grounds to hope that war can and will be abolished.

But do not nations differ in their characters, their interests, and their aims, and does not this difference produce tension which men seek to resolve by aggressive action and ultimately by war?

> The tensions are indeed natural and inevitable, but it is not inevitable that men resolve them through war.

But what evidence have we to believe that they can be resolved peaceably?

> Tensions exist also between individuals and between groups within a nation, yet civil government and patriotic sentiment have curbed the belligerence of individuals and have provided peaceful methods of adjudicating differences.

But that would imply a world-government; and where is there a government that can impose its will on nations and alliances of nations bent on aggression? Even the United Nations does not possess that power.

> It may not possess it today, but this is only a beginning; its very existence, however, is testimony to the earnest concern of the nations with the problem of alternatives to war for resolving international conflicts.

But have the nations the wisdom, the justice, and the good will to subordinate national interests to the welfare of mankind?

> In the teachings of all the great religions, it has been maintained that the ultimate destiny of the human race, the goal set for it by its Creator, is to transcend the self-centered interests of nations and races and to achieve unity and brotherhood.

But that is a matter of faith; can it be proved?

> Faith can be proved, but not by argument; only by deeds. Faith should show itself in the will of the people not to suffer their governments to advance their interests in ways which other nations regard as adverse to their own.

But the United Nations is, after all, composed of nations jealous of their national sovereignty and is it not in danger of breaking up if the will of the majority of nations may be opposed by a militant and aggressive minority?

> That danger exists, and, being aware of it, we must do all in our power to avert it.

But will our own people, or any other powerful people, accept the decisions of an international authority against what it conceives to be its national interests? Has not our whole culture glorified national patriotism as the highest virtue and martial valor as its supreme expression?

> Patriotism is a virtue when it means that love of one's country which takes pride in the country's showing true moral greatness and excelling in creation, not in destruction. The faith of America must repudiate the idolatry of national aggrandizement.

But can we have *freedom* under a world authority?

> Only such an authority can ensure our freedom from want and from fear. Only under law, and by constitutional delegation of power to carry out the common will, have we obtained the liberties we enjoy. Only by the extension of those principles to international relations can we be secure in their enjoyment.

Let there then be an end of doubt and hesitations. Great things have been accomplished by faith. Let us have faith that the God who planted in the human heart the seed of brotherhood and revealed to men their dependence on the law of justice intends the nations to be united and at peace.

> And let us express that faith by our loyal adherence to the Charter of the United Nations, our continuous interest in its improvement and en-

hancement, and our inculcation of fidelity to it through the education of ourselves and our children.

And in that faith let us pray that our generation may not only be spared the scourge of war but be enabled to inaugurate the era of permanent international peace.

AMEN.

Is It a Dream?

Is it a dream—and nothing more—this faith
That nerves our brains to thought—our hands to
      work
For that great day when wars shall cease, and men
Shall live as brothers in a unity
Of love—live in a world made splendid?

Is it a dream—this faith of ours—that pleads
And pulses in our hearts—and bids us look,
Through mists of tears and time, to that great day
When wars shall cease upon the earth, and men
As brothers bound by Love of Man and God,
Shall build a world as gloriously fair
As sunset skies, or mountains when they catch
The farewell kiss of evening on their heights?

—G. A. Studdert-Kennedy

265

The Purposes of the United Nations

On the anniversary of the birth of the United Nations it is fitting that we read the statement of its ideals and aims as formulated in the preamble and the first chapter of its charter. The United Nations is an instrument to effect these aims, a necessarily imperfect instrument, but one that can be perfected, if we remain aware of its fundamental purposes and dedicated to their fulfillment. It is fervently to be hoped that eventually the United Nations may develop into a world government representing all the peoples of the world, guaranteeing their security and their freedom and commanding their devotion and loyalty.

WE, THE PEOPLES OF THE UNITED NA-
TIONS,
determined to save succeeding generations from the scourge of war, which twice in our lifetime has brought untold sorrow to mankind, and

to reaffirm faith in fundamental human rights, in the dignity and worth of the human person, in the equal rights of men and women and of nations large and small, and

to establish conditions under which justice and respect for the obligations arising from treaties and other sources of international law can be maintained, and

to promote social progress and better standards of life in larger freedom, and for these ends, to practice tolerance and live together in peace with one another as good neighbors, and

to unite our strength to maintain international peace and security, and

to ensure, by the acceptance of principles and the institution of methods, that armed force shall not be used, save in the common interest, and

to employ international machinery for the promotion of the economic and social advancement of all peoples,

have resolved to combine our efforts to accomplish these aims.

THE PURPOSES OF THE UNITED NATIONS ARE:

1. To maintain international peace and security, and to that end: to take effective collective measures for the prevention and removal of threats to the peace, and for the suppression of acts of aggression or other breaches of the peace, and to bring about by peaceful means, and in conformity with the principles of justice and international law, adjustment or settlement of international disputes or situations which might lead to a breach of the peace;

2. To develop friendly relations among nations based on respect for the principle of equal rights and self-determination of peoples, and to take other appropriate measures to strengthen universal peace;

3. To achieve international cooperation in solving international problems of an economic, social, cultural, or humanitarian character, and in promoting and encouraging respect for human rights and for fundamental freedoms for all without distinction as to race, sex, language, or religion; and

4. To be a center for harmonizing the actions of nations in the attainment of these common ends.

Build Me a House

Build me a House,
    Said God;
Not of cedar-wood or stone,
Where at some altar-place
Men for their sins atone.
To me, your only sin
Is to build my House too small:
Let there be no dome
To shut out the sky,
Let there be no cumbering wall.
Build me a House, a Home,
In the hearts of hungering men—
Hungering for the bread of hope,
Thirsting for faith, yearning for love,
In a world of grief and pain.
Build me a House!

Build me a World,
    Said God;
Not with a navy's strife,
Nor with a host in arms,
Compassing death, not life.
Build me a World, said God,
Out of man's fairest dreams;
Heaven must be its dome,
Lighted by prophet-gleams;
Justice shall be the stones
On which my World shall rise;
Truth and Love its arches,
Gripping my ageless skies.
Out of dreams, on the earthy sod,
Build me a World,
    Said God.

—*Thomas Curtis Clark*

Education for World Peace

For the United Nations to be effective it is imperative that all the peoples represented in it shall grow in this understanding of what is involved in the task of uniting men and nations for peaceful cooperation. To this end, the United Nations Educational, Scientific and Cultural Organization (UNESCO) was established as one of the most important agencies through which the United Nations does its work. The following selection, which we will read responsively, is adapted from the statement of purposes in the Constitution of UNESCO.

WARS BEGIN in the minds of men; it is in the minds of men, therefore, that the defences of peace must be constructed,

> Throughout the history of mankind, ignorance of each other's ways and lives has been a common cause of that suspicion and mistrust between the peoples of the world through which their differences have all too often broken into war.

The great and terrible world wars of our times were made possible by the denial of the democratic principles of the dignity, equality, and mutual respect of men,

> And by the propagation, in their place, through ignorance and prejudice, of the doctrine of the inequality of men and races.

The wide diffusion of culture, and the education of humanity for justice and liberty and peace are indispensable to the dignity of man.

They constitute a sacred duty which all the nations must fulfill in a spirit of mutual assistance and concern.

A peace based exclusively upon the political and economic arrangements would not be able to secure the unanimous, lasting, and sincere support of the peoples of the world.

To secure such support, the peace must be founded upon the intellectual and moral solidarity of mankind.

To this end, full and equal opportunities for education must be made available to all.

There must be no restriction to the pursuit of objective truth.

The free exchange of ideas and knowledge among people should be facilitated and all means employed for the purposes of mutual understanding and a truer and more perfect knowledge of each other's lives.

Brotherhood*

O Brother man! fold to thy heart thy brother;
    Where pity dwells, the peace of God is there;
To worship rightly is to love each other,
    Each smile a hymn, each kindly deed a prayer.

Follow with reverent steps the great example
    Of Him whose holy work was "doing good";
So shall the wide earth seem our Father's temple,
    Each loving life a psalm of gratitude.

Then shall all shackles fall; the stormy clangor
    Of wild war music o'er the earth shall cease;
Love shall tread out the baleful fire of anger,
    And in its ashes plant the tree of peace!

                    John Greenleaf Whittier

* TO BE SUNG TO THE TUNE OF *"Finlandia."*

Closing Prayer

GOD OF OUR NATION and of all nations, people of different races and different faiths the world over implore Thee in many tongues for the boon of peace. By whatever name men call Thee, and by whatever creed Thou art known to them, Thou art the Power that has implanted in their hearts the yearning for justice, for love, and for peace.

We turn to Thee, ashamed of the sins that have alienated us from Thee and have corrupted the world with injustice, oppression, and war. We repent of the idolatrous worship we have at times accorded to our own national being. We repent of the blasphemy of having invoked Thy name to sanctify acts of ungodly greed and exploitation. Save us from ourselves. Fill our minds with wisdom and our hearts with love, that we may learn to reconcile our wants with those of our neighbors. Teach us to share without strife the blessings Thou dost bestow upon us.

Give us the courage to defend the freedom of the weak against the strong who would enslave them. Grant us the patience to curb our resentments and to submit to arbitration the grievances we bear against our neighbors. Endow us with insight into the needs of other nations and peoples, and inspire us with the love to minister to those needs. Save us from bondage to those fears and passions that involve, in destructive and death-dealing pursuits, the powers which Thou wouldst have us consecrate to Thy service and that of our fellow men.

Help us to build a world government that will command the loyalty of men and women everywhere by its beneficent influence on their lives. Speed the day when nation shall not lift up sword against nation, when men shall no longer train for war, when the burden of armaments shall be lifted from the shoulders of men, and the world shall be full of that knowledge of Thee which will teach us how to live in harmony and love.

AMEN.

**FIRST TUESDAY AFTER THE
FIRST MONDAY IN NOVEMBER**

ELECTION

DAY

A Day Devoted to the Responsibilities of Self-government

The Significance of the Day

ON THIS DAY when we cast our vote for those who are to make our laws and to direct their execution, we seek Thy guidance, O God. We know that unless Thou build the house, in vain do its builders toil, and that unless Thou guard the city, in vain do the guards keep watch. Only when our laws conform to Thy law of justice can they ensure our peace; only when our purposes accord with Thy divine will can our own cause prosper. Inspire us on this day and on every day to make the public good our personal concern, expressed not only by our ballot but by our participation in civic and political movements for promoting the general welfare.

This day the destiny of the nation lies in the hands of us, its citizens. Thou hast charged us with the responsibility to direct that destiny according to Thy will. May the integrity, justice, and beneficence of our government confirm our faith in Thy divine rule. Be Thou with us on this day of decision. Speak to us with the voice of conscience. Overrule any impulse of ours to place personal, sectional, or partisan gain above the general welfare. Make us wise to discern between true worth and its specious semblance, and to choose as our leaders only those who will lead us in paths of righteousness to a future of peace, honor, and well-being. Curb in those whom we shall elect the lust for selfish domination. Strengthen in them the ambition to serve their people faithfully and well. Banish from our hearts ill will and rancor toward those with whom we disagree, so that, whatever be the result of this election, the morrow will see us a united people cooperating loyally for the good of our country and of mankind. AMEN.

The Mission of Democratic Government

THE MISSION OF GOVERNMENT in civilized lands is not alone the exercise of authority, not even of lawful authority; nor is it the rule of the best men, the born heroes and captains of the race, for rarely can such attain to positions of dominance whether elective or dynastic.

> The mission of government is higher than the highest arbitrary rule.

Its mission is to train communities through all their grades, beginning with individuals and ending there again, to rule themselves.

> There is in the possession of a soul by each individual, something so transcendent, so incapable of gradations, that it places all beings on a common level, utterly regardless of the distinctions of intellect, virtue, station, or any height or lowliness whatever.

The highest purpose of democracy does not lie in what it effects directly, for in itself it is perhaps of little account; like Nature, its worth depends on what we see in it and how we use it.

278

But democracy is the best, perhaps the only, means of bringing forth among the masses not merely personalities of grand material achievements but immortal souls.

To be a voter with the rest is not so much; the franchise, like every institution, has its imperfections. But to become an enfranchised man, that is of supreme worth.

To be able to make one's decision count, without humiliation, and equal with all other men, is to commence the grand experiment of development, whose end (perhaps requiring several generations) may be the forming of a full-grown man or woman.

God grant that Americans, in the exercise of their franchise, may learn to govern themselves in accordance with His holy will, that our country may nurture to full growth the souls of all its citizens.

—Adapted from Walt Whitman,
DEMOCRATIC VISTAS

Great Day

Great day!
Great day, de righteous marchin',
Great day!
God's gwine-ter build up Zion's walls.

De chariot rode on de mountain top,
God's gwine-ter build up Zion's walls,
My God he spoke and de chariot stop,
God's gwine-ter build up Zion's walls.

Dis is de day of jubilee,
God's gwine-ter build up Zion's walls,
De Lord has set his people free,
God's gwine-ter build up Zion's walls.

Gwine take my breas'-plate, sword in han',
God's gwine-ter build up Zion's walls,
An' march out boldly, in-a de field,
God's gwine-ter build up Zion's walls.

We want no cowards in our ban',
God's gwine-ter build up Zion's walls,
We call for valiant hearted men,
God's gwine-ter build up Zion's walls.

Great day!
Great day, de righteous marchin',
Great day!
God's gwine-ter build up Zion's walls.*

—*Anonymous*

* THE MUSIC FOR THIS SONG IS TO BE FOUND IN *The Books of American Negro Spirituals* (VOLUME 2, PAGE 56), EDITED BY J. W. JOHNSON AND J. ROSAMOND JOHNSON, PUBLISHED BY THE VIKING PRESS, NEW YORK.

Who Serves His Country Best

He serves his country best
Who lives pure life, and doeth righteous deed,
And walks straight paths, however others stray.
And leaves his sons as uttermost bequest
A stainless record which all men may read.

No drop but serves the slowly lifting tide,
No dew but has an errand to some flower,
No smallest star but sheds some helpful ray,
And man by man, each giving to all the rest,
Makes the firm bulwark of the country's power.

—*Susan Coolidge*

Democratic Leadership

THE HOPE OF THE UNITED STATES, in the present and in the future, is the hope and confidence that out of unknown homes will come men who will constitute themselves the masters of industry and of politics.

The hopefulness, the welfare, the enterprise, the initiative of the ordinary American citizen are the only things that make the United States rich.

America does not consist politically of the men who set themselves up to be political leaders; she does not consist of the men who do most of her talking—they are important only so far as they speak for that great voiceless multitude of men, the great body and the saving force of the nation.

> Nobody who cannot speak the common thought, who does not move by the common impulse, is the man to speak for America.

Only he is fit to speak who knows the thoughts of the great body of citizens, the men who go about their business every day, the men who toil from morning till night, the men who go home tired in the evenings, the men who are carrying on the things we are so proud of.

> The great glory of our land is that nobody can predict from what family, from what region, from what race, even, the leaders of the country are going to come.

The only way that government is kept pure is by keeping those channels open by which humble people rise to power, so that there will constantly be coming new blood into the veins of the body politic.

> We must keep open the channels by which obscure men may break the crust of any class to which they happen to belong, may spring up to higher levels and be counted among the leaders of the state.

Let this nation ever remember that a people shall be saved by the power that sleeps in its own deep bosom, or by none; shall be renewed in hope, in conscience, in strength, by waters welling up from its own sweet, perennial springs.

It shall not be saved from above, by patronage of its aristocrats; for the flower does not bear the root, but the root the flower.

What some call the radicalism of our times is simply the effort of nature to release the generous energies of our people.

Our people are at bottom just, virtuous, and hopeful; the roots of its being are in the soil of what is lovely, pure, and of good report.

We therefore need have no fear of a radicalism that is designed to clear a way for the realization of the aspirations of a sturdy people.

For that nation is best served which affords to all its citizens the amplest opportunity to give the best of themselves to its service.

—*Adapted from Woodrow Wilson*, THE NEW FREEDOM

All Citizens Are Trustees
of the Public Welfare

To be elected president of the United States is to be invested with great power and responsibility. Well may a president, on his inauguration, be awed by the powers delegated to him by the electorate. No human being could hope to discharge such responsibility unless he could count on the cooperation of those whom he has been elected to serve. These sentiments were eloquently voiced by President Grover Cleveland in his first inaugural address.

IN THE DISCHARGE of my official duty I shall endeavor to be guided by a just and proper construction of the Constitution, a careful observance of the distinction between the powers granted to the Federal Government and those reserved to the States or to the people, and by a cautious appreciation of those functions which by the Constitution and laws have been assigned to the executive branches of the government.

But the man who takes the oath today to preserve, protect, and defend the Constitution of the United States only assumes the solemn obligation which every patriotic citizen—on the farm, in the workshop, in the busy marts of trade and everywhere—should share with him. The Constitution which prescribes his oath, my countryman, is yours; the government you have chosen him to administer for a time is yours; the laws and the entire scheme of our civil rule, from the town meeting to the State capitals and the national capital, is yours. Every voter, as surely as your chief magistrate, under the same high sanction, though in a different sphere, exercises a public trust. Nor is this all. Every citizen owes to the country a vigilant watch and close scrutiny of its public servants and a fair and reasonable estimate of their fidelity and usefulness. Thus is the people's will impressed upon the whole framework of our civil polity—municipal, state, and federal; and this is the price of our liberty and the inspiration of our faith in the republic.

Greatness Resides in the Citizen, Not in the Government

The sum of all known reverence I add up in you who-
    ever you are.
The President is there in the White House for you,
    it is not you who are here for him.
The Secretaries act in their bureaus for you, not you
    here for them.
The Congress convenes every Twelfth-month for you.

Laws, courts, the forming of States, the charters of cities, the going and coming of commerce and mails, are all for the people.

The place where a great city stands is not the place of stretch'd wharves, docks, manufactures, deposits of produce merely,

Nor the place of the tallest and costliest buildings or shops selling goods from the rest of the earth,

Nor the place of the most numerous population.

Where the city stands with the brawniest breed of
 orators and bards,
Where the city stands that is belov'd by these, and
 loves them in return and understands them,

 Where the men and women think lightly of the
  laws,

Where the slave ceases, and the master of slaves
 ceases,

 Where the populace rise at once against the
  never-ending audacity of elected persons,

Where the citizen is always the head and ideal, and
 President, Mayor, Governor and what not,
 are agents for pay,

 Where children are taught to depend on themselves,

Where equanimity is illustrated in affairs,
Where speculations of the soul are encouraged,

 Where women walk in public processions in the
  streets the same as the men,
 Where they enter the public assembly and take
  places the same as the men,

Where the city of the faithfulest friends stands,
Where the city of the cleanliness of the sexes stands,

Where the city of the healthiest fathers stands,
Where the city of the best-bodied mothers stands,
There the great city stands.

—*Adapted from Walt Whitman*, A
Song for Occupations and song of
the broad axe

The True Leader Too Often Abused

When the mighty Maccabean led the armies of the
Lord,
And the cohorts of Nicanor feared the red Judean
sword,
Though he bore a people's sorrows, though he periled
life and fame,
Like the shrilling of the locust rose the bitter cry of
blame,
With the murmur and the clamor and the hiss and hoot
and groan
Of the narrow clan that fancy all hearts evil, save their
own:
"Ah! he fought upon the Sabbath!—broke the law of
hearth and home!
Down with Judas Maccabeus! who would sell the land
to Rome!"
So they left that noble leader in their envy and
their pride,

And he fell, for them, in battle. He was happy
    that he died.

Seven years the Great Virginian faced the legions of the
    king,
Braving with his ragged heroes, warfare's rage and
    winter's sting,—
Strong in peril, calm in triumph, lion-hearted through
    despair,
Till the cloud of conflict lifted and a new-born flag was
    there.
Through the smoke of field and bivouac, yea, when
    armed strife was done
And he toiled to weld a nation of the realms his sword
    had won,
Came the cry of hate and malice fostered by the
    poisoned pen:
"Dotard! traitor! false usurper!" brawled the breed
    of little men.
    Peace! the Canon of the Ages echoes not the ass's
      bray.
    While his name resounds forever, his defamers—
      who were they?

Noble, wise, and simple-hearted, rock against a
    hundred jars,
Lincoln wrought with constant purpose to unite the
    sundered Stars.
Who may guess his burning anguish that his hand,
    which sought to heal,
First must wound what most he cherished—search the
    land with flame and steel!
Ever when his need was sorest, loud the spiteful cry
    uprose;

Fiercely, bitterly they chorused, feigned friends and
    open foes,
Every action misconstruing, every motive splashing
    back,
Every mouth its venom spewing, "Butcher! tyrant!"
    yelped the pack,
    Till the murderous bullet smote him and he died
    as martyrs die;
    And a nation's wail of mourning gave those
    dastard throats the lie.

Think! ye shrill and frequent carpers, jealous of the
    public weal,
Truly, may not they who govern love their land with
    equal zeal?
May not those who work in silence build in fact a noble
    dream?
Free your hearts of cant and rancor! Purge your souls
    of self-esteem!
Delve no more in petty errors till your eyes are dim
    with dust!
View with broader, clearer vision; seek to fathom,
    learn to trust.
Hail! true souls that, uncomplaining, take the truth of
    foe and friend,
Fearless front the hidden danger! Ye shall triumph at
    the end.
    For the men that do are deathless, spite of scoff
    and sneer and curse,
    While the snarlers are forgotten,—or
    remembered, which is worse.

Arthur Guiterman,
THE SNARLERS

No Racial Bar to Self-Government

Democracy involves universal suffrage. The achievement of that suffrage, even in the United States, did not come about at once. Even today it is, in places, nullified by legal subterfuges. In the early days of our Republic, the one great barrier to the attainment of true self-government was Negro slavery. The issue became acute when the United States acquired vast new territories and the question was raised whether slavery should be permitted or forbidden in them. It was debated in the Senatorial campaign in Illinois, in which Stephen Douglas and Abraham Lincoln were opposing candidates. Douglas held that the territories should, on the principle of self-government, decide for themselves whether slavery should be permitted in their borders or not. The view that Lincoln took is expressed in the following excerpt from one of his debates with Douglas.

THE DOCTRINE of self-government is right—absolutely and eternally right—but it has not just application as here attempted. Or perhaps I should say that whether it has such application depends upon whether a Negro *is not* or *is* a man. If he is not a man, in that case he who is a man may as a matter of self-government do just what he pleases with him.

But if the Negro is a man, is it not to that extent a total destruction of self-government to say that he too shall not govern himself? When the white man governs himself, that is self-government; but when he governs himself and also governs another man, that is more than self-government—that is despotism. If the Negro is a man, why then my ancient faith teaches me that "all men are created equal," and that there can be no moral right in connection with one man's making a slave of another.

Judge Douglas frequently, with bitter irony and sarcasm, paraphrases our argument by saying: "The white people of Nebraska are good enough to govern themselves, but they are not good enough to govern a few miserable Negroes!"

Well! I doubt not that the people of Nebraska are and will continue to be as good as the average of people elsewhere. I do not say the contrary. What I do say is that no man is good enough to govern another man without the other's consent. I say this is the leading principle, the sheet-anchor of American republicanism. Our Declaration of Independence says:

"We hold these truths to be self-evident: That all men are created equal; that they are endowed by their Creator with certain unalienable rights; that among these are life, liberty and the pursuit of happiness. That to secure these rights, governments are instituted among men, *deriving their just powers from the consent of the governed.*"

I have quoted so much at this time merely to show that, according to our ancient faith, the just powers of governments are derived from the consent of the governed. Now the relation of master and slave is a total violation of this principle. The master not only governs the slave without his consent, but he governs him by a set of rules altogether different from those which he prescribes for himself. Allow all the governed an equal voice in the government, and that, and that only, is self-government.

Walk Together Children*

Walk together children,
Don't you get weary,
Walk together children,
Don't you get weary,
Oh, talk together children,
Don't you get weary,
There's a great camp meeting in the Promised Land.

Oh, sing together children,
Don't you get weary,
Sing together children,
Don't you get weary,
Oh, shout together children,
Don't you get weary,
There's a great camp meeting in the Promised Land.

Gwine ter mourn and never tire;
Mourn and never tire.
Mourn and never tire;
There's a great camp meeting in the Promised Land.
REPEAT

Oh, get you ready children,
Don't you get weary,
Get you ready children,
Don't you get weary,
We'll enter there,
Oh, children, don't you get weary,
There's a great camp meeting in the Promised Land.

—Anonymous

* THE MUSIC FOR THIS SONG IS TO BE FOUND IN *The Books of American Negro Spirituals* (VOLUME 2, PAGE 180), EDITED BY J. W. JOHNSON AND J. ROSAMOND JOHNSON, PUBLISHED BY THE VIKING PRESS, NEW YORK.

Education for Democracy

THE RIGHT OF SELF-GOVERNMENT implies the duty to seek the knowledge which will enable us to govern ourselves wisely. Public education that is honest and devoted to the common good is indispensable to democracy. What then should be the goals of education for democracy?

> We must recognize the threat to democracy in demands for retrenchment in education, in attacks on the Bill of Rights, in gag laws, in censorship of teachers and journalists, in racial and religious intolerance, in those newspapers which make profit or power their chief goal.

If we are to be "one nation, indivisible, with liberty and justice for all," our schools must provide liberty and justice for all, without discrimination on account of poverty, sex, race, or religion.

> Our teachers must be trained in their responsibilities; they must be devoted to the principles of democracy and intellectual freedom; they must be free to inculcate their enthusiasm in the minds of the young.

Our children and our adults must receive full moral and material assistance in their pursuit of knowledge.

> Our basic civil liberties of speech, press, assembly, and teaching must be protected.

Our schools, press, and radio must present the facts, and the truth behind the facts, about our history and traditions, about the world in which we live, about race and culture, without fear or malice, without suppression or distortion.

May our educators in a democratic society keep free the channels of knowledge so that our people can examine all the facts that should govern our political decisions with the critical spirit necessary for an intelligent appraisal and choice.

Then will our country do its part to preserve and extend the democratic heritage for the good of all mankind.

—*Adapted from New York Chapter, American Committee for Democracy and Intellectual Freedom,* MANIFESTO OF EDUCATORS

Democracy the Test of Civilization

Every citizen has the duty to use his ballot to enhance the true greatness of the nation, to advance its civilization. But what distinguishes an advanced civilization from a retarded one? Let us listen to the counsel of that American sage Ralph Waldo Emerson.

IF THERE BE A COUNTRY which cannot stand any one of these tests,—a country where knowledge cannot be diffused without perils of mob law and statute law; where speech is not free; where the post-office is violated, mail-bags opened and letters tampered with; where public liberty is attacked in the primary institution of social life; where the position of the white woman is injuriously affected by the outlawry of the black woman; where the arts, such as they have, are all imported, having no indigenous life; where the laborer is not secure in the earnings of his own hands; where suffrage is not free or equal;—that country is, in all these respects, not civil, but barbarous; and no advantages of soil, climate or coast can resist these suicidal mischiefs.

Morality and all the incidents of morality are essential; as, justice to the citizen, and personal liberty. Montesquieu says: "Countries are well cultivated, not as they are fertile, but as they are free"; and the remark holds not less but more true of the culture of men than of the tillage of land. And the highest proof of civility is that the whole public action of the State is directed on securing the greatest good of the greatest number.

A Poet's Dream for His City

The foundation of our national democracy is the exercise of local self-government. Pride in our city, cooperation with neighbors in making it worthy of pride, are the source from which our national life draws its strength. It is therefore fitting on this occasion that we read of the dream that the American poet, Vachel Lindsay, cherished for his city.

Let not our town be large, remembering
That little Athens was the Muses' home,
That Oxford rules the heart of London still,
That Florence gave the Renaissance to Rome.

Record it for the grandson of your son—
A city is not builded in a day:
Our little town cannot complete her soul
Till countless generations pass away.

Now let each child be joined as to a church
To her perpetual hopes, each man ordained:
Let every street be made a reverent aisle
Where Music grows and Beauty is unchained.

Let Science and Machinery and Trade
Be slaves of her, and make her all in all,
Building against our blatant, restless time
An unseen, skilful medieval wall.

We should build parks that students from afar
Would choose to starve in, rather than go home,

Fair little squares, with Phidian ornament,
Food for the spirit, milk and honeycomb.

Songs shall be sung by us in that good day,
Songs we have written, blood within the rhyme,
Beating as when Old England still was glad,—
The purple, rich Elizabethan time.

Say, is my prophecy too fair and far?
I only know, unless her faith be high,
The soul of this, our Nineveh, is doomed,
Our little Babylon will surely die.

The genius of the Maple, Elm and Oak,
The secret hidden in each grain of corn,
The glory that the prairie angels sing
At night when sons of Life and Love are born,—

When will they start our vulgar blood athrill
With living language, words that set us free?
When will they make a path of beauty clear
Between our riches and our liberty?

We must have many Lincoln-hearted men.
A city is not builded in a day.
And they must do their work, and come and go,
While countless generations pass away.

America, the Beautiful

O beautiful for spacious skies,
For amber waves of grain,
For purple mountain majesties
Above the fruited plain!
America! America!
God shed His grace on thee,
And crown thy good with brotherhood,
From sea to shining sea!

O beautiful for pilgrim feet
Whose stern impassioned stress
A thorough-fare for freedom beat
Across the wilderness!
America! America!
God mend thine ev'ry flaw,
Confirm thy soul in self-control,
Thy liberty in law!

O beautiful for heroes proved
In liberating strife,
Who more than self their country loved,
And mercy more than life!
America! America!
May God thy gold refine,
Till all success be nobleness,
And ev'ry gain divine!

O beautiful for patriot dream
That sees beyond the years
Thine alabaster cities gleam
Undimmed by human tears!

America! America!
God shed His grace on thee,
And crown thy good with brotherhood,
From sea to shining sea!

—*Katherine Lee Bates*

The Citizen's Highest Privilege and Most Solemn Duty

We may well conclude this assembly by giving heed to the message of one of America's great presidents on the eve of election. In his final radio address at the end of the 1940 campaign, President Franklin Delano Roosevelt turned from a discussion of controversial issues to voice his deep sense of the solemn meaning of Election Day. This is his message.

IN THIS TOWN, as in every community in our nation, friends and neighbors will gather together around the polling place.

They will discuss the state of the nation, the weather, and the prospect for their favorite football team. They will discuss the political campaign. And I suppose there will be a few warm arguments.

But when you and I step into the voting booth, we can proudly say: "I am an American, and this vote I am casting is the exercise of my highest privilege and my most solemn duty to my country."

We vote as free men, impelled only by the urgings of our own wisdom and our own conscience.

In our polling places are no storm troopers or secret police to look over our shoulders as we mark our ballots.

In every political campaign the question on which we all finally pass judgment is simply this: "Who do I think is the candidate best qualified to act as President, or Governor, or Senator, or Mayor, or Supervisor, or County Commissioner during the next term?"

It is that right, the right to determine for themselves who should be their own officers of government that provides for the people the most powerful safeguard of our democracy.

Dictators have forgotten—or perhaps they never knew—that the opinion of all the people, freely formed and freely expressed, without fear or coercion, is wiser than the opinion of any one man or any small group of men.

We have more faith in the collective opinion of all Americans than in the individual opinion of any one American.

Every one of us has a continuing responsibility for the Government which we choose.

Democracy is not just a word, to be shouted at political rallies and then put back into the dictionary after election day.

The service of democracy must be something much more than mere lip-service.

It is a living thing—a human thing—compounded of brains and muscle and heart and soul. The service of democracy is the birthright of every citizen, the White and the Colored; the Protestant, the Catholic and the Jew; the sons and daughters of every country in the world, who make up the people of the land.

Freedom of speech is of no use to the man who has nothing to say and, freedom of worship is of no use to the man who has lost his God. A free election is of no use to the man who is too indifferent to vote.

Tomorrow you will decide for yourselves how the legislative and executive branches of your country are to be run during their next terms and by whom.

After the ballots are counted, the real rulers of this country will have had their way.

After the ballots are counted, the United States of America will still be united.

We people of America know that man cannot live by bread alone.

We know that we have a reservoir of religious strength which can withstand attacks from abroad and corruption from within.

On this election eve, we all have in our hearts and minds a prayer for the dignity, the integrity and the peace of our beloved country.

Therefore I believe that you will find it fitting that I read to you an old prayer which asks the guidance of God for our nation:

*The assembly rise
and, in unison with the leader, join
in the reading of the prayer
in which Roosevelt led the nation*

ALMIGHTY GOD, who hast given us this good land for our heritage; We beseech Thee that we may always prove ourselves a people mindful of Thy favor and glad to do Thy will. Bless our land with honorable industry, sound learning, and pure manners. Save us from violence, discord, and confusion; from pride and arrogancy, and from every evil way. Defend our liberties, and fashion into one united people the multitudes brought hither out of many kindreds and tongues. Endue with the spirit of wisdom those to whom, in Thy name, we entrust the authority of government, that there may be justice and peace at home, and that, through obedience to Thy law, we may show forth Thy praise among the nations of the earth. In the time of prosperity, fill our hearts with thankfulness, and in the day of trouble, suffer not our trust in Thee to fail. AMEN

FOURTH THURSDAY IN NOVEMBER

THANKSGIVING

DAY

A Day Devoted to a Grateful Awareness of the Blessings of American Life

The Significance of the Day

OUR GOD AND FATHER, it is good to give thanks to Thee and to acknowledge Thy blessings. Only thus can we savor them to the full. In the hurried pace of our lives and in our preoccupation with the petty and the trivial, we are prone to take Thy gifts for granted. Oblivious of Thy bounties, we sinfully waste the opportunities they afford us for living the good life. Therefore, do we set aside this day for thanksgiving.

We thank Thee for the land and for its fruits by which we live. We thank Thee for the vigor of body and mind that enables us to exploit the fertility of our country's fields and forests and the buried treasures of its mineral wealth. We thank Thee for the varied beauty of its landscape, for the grandeur of its mountains, the hospitality of its plains and prairies, and the gleaming vistas of ocean from its coasts.

We thank Thee for the inspiration of our country's history—for the courage and hardihood that sustained its explorers and pioneers, for the heroism that inspires its fighters for freedom and equality, for the enterprise that builds its teeming cities, for the arts that express the beauty and meaning of its way of life, for the just laws and free institutions that enable its people to work together in peace and harmony.

Grant, O God, in Thy grace, that we may perfect our national life to the measure of Thy bounty. Grateful for the gifts Thou hast bestowed upon us, may we use them to extend the area of freedom, justice, and good-will among men. May our use of Thy gifts bear witness to mankind that life is good when lived according to Thy benign will, O gracious Giver of all good. AMEN.

Thanksgiving as an Expression
of the American Spirit

THIS OLDEST FESTIVAL, dating from the heroic age of America, is the best expression of our national spirit.

It combines into one conception productive enterprise, domestic felicity, and religious devotion.

Thanksgiving Day represents the fruits of industry turned to family festivity and sanctified by prayer.

It was instituted by men of culture and women of refinement, who showed themselves willing to suffer persecution, imprisonment, banishment from the comforts of an English home, exile across the sea, cold, hunger, pestilence, and death for their principles.

Those principles are today the richest treasure and the brightest hope for humanity.

They are the stuff of which heroes were made and by which a nation was nurtured to its manhood.

These three principles are the legacy which that heroic age has bequeathed to us, its heirs: *self-government in the state, freedom for the Church, good will toward mankind.*

Let us cherish these principles, for in them lie the essence, the beauty, the strength of American institutions, and the warrant of their perpetuity.

—*Adapted from Joseph Parrish Thompson*

O God, Beneath Thy Guiding Hand *

O God, beneath Thy guilding hand
Our exiled fathers crossed the sea;
And when they trod the wint'ry strand,
With pray'r and psalm they worshiped Thee.

Thou heard'st, well pleased, the song, the pray'r
Thy blessing came, and still its Pow'r
Shall onward through all ages bear
The mem'ry of that holy hour.

And here thy name, O God of love,
Their children's children shall adore,
Till these eternal hills remove,
And spring adorns the earth no more.

—*Leonard Bacon*

* THE MUSIC FOR THIS SONG IS TO BE FOUND IN *Assembly Songs and Choruses* (PAGE 51), EDITED BY RANDALL J. CONDON, HELEN S. LEAVITT, ELBRIDGE W. NEWTON, PUBLISHED BY GINN AND COMPANY, BOSTON.

Harvest Hymn

Once more the liberal year laughs out
 O'er richer stores than gems of gold;
Once more with harvest song and shout
 Is nature's boldest triumph told.

Our common mother rests and sings
 Like Ruth among her garnered sheaves;
Her lap is full of goodly things,
 Her brow is bright with autumn leaves.

Oh, favors old, yet ever new,
 Oh, blessing with the sunshine sent!
The bounty overruns our due,
 The fullness shames our discontent.

We shut our eyes, the bowers bloom on;
 We murmur, but the corn ears fill;
We choose the shadow, but the sun
 That casts it shines behind us still,

And gives us, with our rugged soil,
 The power to make it Eden fair,
And richer fruits to crown our toil,
 Than summer-wedded islands bear.

Who murmurs at his lot today?
 Who scorns his native fruit and bloom,
Or sighs for dainties far away,
 Besides the bounteous boards of home?

Thank heaven, instead, that freedom's arm
  Can change a rocky soil to gold;
That brave and generous lives can warm
  A clime with northern ices cold.

And by the altars wreathed with flowers,
  And fields with fruits awake again
Thanksgiving for the golden hours,
  The earlier and the latter rain.

—*John Greenleaf Whittier*

Now Sing We a Song*

Now sing we a song for the harvest;
Thanksgiving and honor and praise,
For all that the bountiful Giver
Hath given to gladden our days;

For grasses of upland and lowland,
For fruits of the garden and field,
For gold which the mine and the furrow
To delver and husbandman yield.

And thanks for the harvest of beauty,
For that which the hands cannot hold;
The harvest, eyes only can gather,
And only our hearts can enfold.

We reap it on mountain and moorland,
We glean it from meadow and lea,
We garner it in from the cloudland,
We bind it in sheaves from the sea. Amen.

—*John W. Chadwick*

* THE MUSIC FOR THIS SONG IS TO BE FOUND IN *Hymns for the Living Age* (PAGE 81), EDITED BY H. AUGUSTINE SMITH, PUBLISHED BY THE FLEMING H. REVELL COMPANY, NEW YORK.

How the Nation Can Best Show Its Gratitude

ONCE AGAIN THE SEASON OF THE YEAR HAS COME WHEN, in accordance with the custom of our forefathers for generations past, we are called upon to give praise and thanksgiving to God.

During the past year we have been free from famine, from pestilence, from war. We are at peace with all the rest of mankind.

Our natural resources are abundant, and we have been endowed with adequate knowledge to make good use of these resources.

Ours is the opportunity as a free people to develop to the fullest extent all our powers of body, of mind, and of that which stands above both body and mind—of character.

Much has been given us from on high, and much will rightly be expected of us in return.

Into our care these resources of nature have been entrusted, and we are not to be pardoned either if we squander and waste them, or yet if we leave them undeveloped, for they must be made fruitful in our hands.

Ever through the ages, at all times and among all peoples, prosperity has been fraught with danger, and it behooves us to beseech the Giver of all things that we may not fall into love of ease and luxury,

That we may not lose our sense of moral responsibility, that we may not forget our duty to God, and to our neighbor.

Our democracy, based upon the principles of orderly liberty, can be perpetuated only if, in the heart of its citizens, there dwells a keen sense of righteousness and justice.

Let us pray that this spirit of righteousness and justice may grow in the hearts of all of us. May our souls be ever inclined toward the virtues that tell for gentleness and tenderness, for loving-kindness and forbearance, one toward another.

May our souls be inclined also toward those no less necessary virtues that make for manliness and rugged hardihood;

For only by love and patience, courage and fortitude can either nation or individual rise to the
level of greatness.

Let us then as a people set our faces resolutely against
evil, and with broad charity, with kindness and good
will toward all men, but with unflinching determination
to smite down wrong, let us strive with all the strength
that is given us for righteousness in public and in private life.

—*Adapted from Theodore Roosevelt*

A Thanksgiving Proclamation
of George Washington

*The custom of proclaiming a day of national
thanksgiving for the blessings that God has
showered on America was initiated by its first
president, George Washington. Let us read from
his proclamation. It will help to make us aware
of the great heritage of blessing which is ours by
virtue of our being the heirs of those generous
laws and institutions which the Founding Fathers
of our country endeavored to bequeath to posterity.*

WHEREAS it is the duty of all nations to acknowledge the providence of Almighty God, to obey His
will, to be grateful for His benefits and humbly to implore His protection and favor; and whereas both

Houses of Congress have, by their joint committee, requested me to recommend to the people of the United States a day of public thanksgiving and prayer, to be observed by acknowledging with grateful hearts the many and signal favors of Almighty God, especially by affording them an opportunity peaceably to establish a form of government for their safety and happiness;

NOW THEREFORE, I do recommend and assign Thursday, the twenty-sixth day of November next, to be devoted by the people of these States to the service of that great and glorious Being, who is the beneficent Author of all the good that was, that is, or that will be; that we may then all unite in rendering unto him our sincere and humble thanks for His kind care and protection of the people of this country, previous to their becoming a nation; for the signal and manifold mercies, and the favorable interpositions of His providence in the course and conclusion of the late war; for the great degree of tranquility, union and plenty, which we have since enjoyed; for the peaceable and rational manner in which we have been enabled to establish Constitutions of government for our safety and happiness and particularly the national one now lately instituted; for the civil and religious liberty with which we are blessed, and the means we have of acquiring and diffusing useful knowledge; and, in general, for all the great and various favors, which He has been pleased to confer upon us.

And also that we may then unite in most humbly offering our prayers and supplications to the great Lord and Ruler of Nations, and beseech Him to pardon our national and other transgressions; to enable us all, whether in public or private stations, to perform our several and relative duties properly and punctually; to render our National Government a blessing to all the peoples, by constantly being a government of wise, just and constitutional laws, discreetly and faithfully executed and obeyed; to protect and guide all sovereigns and nations (especially such as have shown kindness to us) and to bless them with good governments, peace and concord; to promote the knowledge and practice of true religion and virtue, and the increase of science among them and us; and, generally, to grant unto all mankind such a degree of temporal prosperity as He alone knows to be best.

O God, Our Help in Ages Past *

O God, our help in ages past
Our hopes for years to come,
Our shelter from the stormy blast
And our eternal home!

Before the hills in order stood,
Or earth received her frame,
From everlasting Thou art God,
To endless years the same.

A thousand ages in Thy sight
Are like an evening gone;
Short as the watch that ends the night
Before this rising sun.

O God, our help in ages past,
Our hope for years to come,
Be thou our guard while life shall last,
And our eternal home.

—*Isaac Watts*

* THE MUSIC FOR THIS SONG IS TO BE FOUND IN *Assembly Songs and Choruses* (PAGE 223), EDITED BY RANDALL J. CONDON, HELEN S. LEAVITT, AND ELBRIDGE W. NEWTON, PUBLISHED BY GINN AND COMPANY, BOSTON.

Gratitude for the Diversity of American Culture

ON THIS DAY of national thanksgiving, we are grateful to God not only for those benefits that have come to us from this land and from our experience in its settlement and development but also for the gifts that the settlers in this country brought with them from the lands of their origin. For we are the children of all the old nations, bound together by all that is good in many heritages.

Those who have here sought a haven and refuge, from the first settlers in Jamestown and in Plymouth to the last shipload of immigrants, came not empty-handed but bearing cultural gifts.

We are grateful for the gifts brought to this country by the sturdy stock that came from old England—

315

For their gift of the language that we all speak and that unites all of us, for their gift of civic liberty and for the freedom of worship that they planted and fostered in this land.

But not from England alone stem those blessings that make us thank Thee for having cast our lot in this blessed land.

The pattern of America is a blend of culture from many lands, woven of threads from many corners of the world.

Diversity itself is the pattern of America, the very stuff and color of its fabric.

To reap the full benefit of that diversity we should seek to know more about the experiences and qualities, hopes and achievements of the many kinds of people who have made America.

Not until wave after wave of these facts sweeps over us will the true quality of our American life ring in the American atmosphere, the American consciousness.

Only then will all Americans feel themselves at one with the builders of America in the past and with each other in the present, drawn together, knit together by a common stake in America.

Then all over the country, from the Atlantic to the Pacific, from the Canadian to the Mexican border, Swedish Americans, Russian, German, Italian, Irish, Negro, French, Spanish, Oriental, Czech Americans will feel the same warmth and pride in their old yellowing letters and documents which is felt by those descended from the passengers of the Mayflower.

Then will they all feel themselves at home in the history of America, in that interplay, that diversity which *is* America.

The cultural atmosphere of the United States will then mean new and broader ways of seeing one's neighbor and freer and more generous ways of behaving toward him.

It will mean a new solidarity, irrespective of background, one that lets people remain themselves.

It will bring into full play the healthy simultaneous tension and fusion of stubborn creative differences, challenging all groups and individuals to vie with one another in contributing from their own life to the good of all.

Open Thou our eyes, O God, that we may see Thine image in all men and accept humbly and gratefully the gifts that each race, creed and nationality brings to our American life.

Then let us gather in one sheaf all these gifts and lay them on the altar of America's consecration to the service of Thee and Thy kingdom of freedom, justice and peace.

—*Suggested by Louis Adamic,*
A NATION OF NATIONS

317

Thanksgiving

To Be Recited in Unison

I thank Thee that I learn
Not toil to spurn;
With all beneath the sun
It makes me one;—
For tears, whereby I gain
Kinship with human pain;
For love, my comrade by the dusty ways,
I give Thee praise.

—Emily Read Jones

Thanksgiving in Hard Times

To feel grateful when all things seem to be working out to our satisfaction is easy, but it is precisely when many of our desires are thwarted that we need most to be made aware of the blessings we enjoy, blessings that justify our hope in the future. The religious soul has always been able to find occasion for gratitude in adversity no less than in prosperity. The following reflections, suggested by the observance of Thanksgiving in a year of depression, should help us to be truly thankful whether fortune has smiled or frowned upon us.

A THOUGHTFUL MIND will perceive propriety in a service of thanksgiving on the ground, not only of any exceptional benefit, but of the continuance of those ordinary blessings which give its gladness and beauty to life. The preservation of our life itself from casualty or from disease, which might have fallen upon it, is no less a sign of God's goodness than a narrow escape from what seemed certain death. And so, though any given year may not have been marked by what we should call conspicuous blessings, it is right and proper that we should meet to give thanks for that bounty of heaven which has not failed, for our personal life, and health, and happiness, for the undisturbed serenity and tranquility of our homes, for the maintenance of public order, content and liberty, for the peaceful progress of industry, for the regular and beneficent operations of nature. The hand of God is in all this, as well as in the events which more strikingly exhibit His goodness and His power . . .

The year that is ending has not been what we commonly call a "good" year. It has been rather a bad year in the history of other nations, in business and in politics within our own borders.

How then shall we meet the call which invites us to give thanks today to God for His goodness. We might try to banish from our minds these gloomy facts. . . . And yet it is more likely to be useful to look at the facts as they are and to ask whether, if we should judge them aright, we should not find, not in spite of them, but *in* them, traces and tokens of God's goodness and occasions for praise.

We mourn, for example, the decline of our material prosperity, but it is a shallow view of things which regards material prosperity as an unmixed good for a man or for a nation. The psalmist who said, "It is good for me that I have been afflicted," uttered a truth

which finds abundant confirmation in national as well
as in personal history. Look at your neighbor whom
you knew as a poor boy and who now is worth his millions. . . . He used to be considerate of others, helpful to those who needed help, nobly generous with
what little he had to give. Now he seems to think that
poverty is a crime, and it is easier to get a flame out
of an iceberg than a dollar out of his purse. Once he
judged men by their moral character. Now he speaks
of them as "worth" whatever their property would
sell for in the market. . . . What has made the
change in him? Nothing but his success. . . .

And the same thing is equally true of a nation. The
unparalleled development of the material resources of
the American people in recent years has astonished the
world, but it has also awakened the gravest solicitude
of thoughtful minds. The ever rising tide of wealth,
the vast increase and wide diffusion of luxury, the
reckless extravagance and waste which have been common, the senseless rivalry in vulgar display, the growing tyranny of money in the hands of rich men and rich
corporations, the wild fever of speculation, the prosti-
tution of public office to an unrestrained desire of
wealth, the increased inequality, and, in consequence of
this, the deepening animosity of the classes of which
society is composed, the swift and shameless spread of
corruption in politics, the intrusion into the place of
legitimate and honest business of the methods and
morals of the gambling room, the growing fre-
quency of gross violations of trust—all these things
. . . have come as the direct and inevitable fruit
of the era of prosperity which now—for a time at least,
is ended. . . .

As you try to gather up your reasons for thanksgiving, do not turn your thoughts away from the things which at first seem dark. . . . Look at them, rather, frankly . . . and see if the goodness and the mercy of God are not manifest in them. So may your sorrows be turned into joy, and your sore disappointment into confident hope. So may you gain the height of adoring trust whereon he stood who long ago declared: "I will bless the Lord at all time: His praise shall continually be in my mouth."

—*Edward B. Coe*

One Kind of Humility

Shall we say heaven is not heaven
Since golden stairs are rugged and uneven?

    Or that no light illuminates a star
    That swings in other regions than we are?

Deny with sour breath enduring God
Because we cling so rankly to the sod?

    No. Cleansed with weeping, fasting, and with
        prayer
    Praise God. Look starward. Mount the stair.

—*Jean Starr Untermeyer,*
STEEP ASCENT

Come, Ye Thankful People, Come*

Come, ye thankful people, come,
Raise the song of harvest home;
All is safely gathered in,
Ere the winter storms begin;
God, our Maker, doth provide
For our wants to be supplied;
Come to God's own temple, come,
Raise the song of harvest home.

—*Henry Alford*

* THE MUSIC FOR THIS SONG IS TO BE FOUND IN *Assembly Songs and Choruses* (PAGE 214), EDITED BY RANDALL J. CONDON, HELEN S. LEAVITT, AND ELBRIDGE W. NEWTON, PUBLISHED BY GINN AND COMPANY, BOSTON.

The Blessings of Home

Of all the national festivals of America, Thanksgiving is most commonly celebrated by festivities and ritual observances in the home. This is natural, for any reflection on the blessings for which we are most grateful naturally brings to mind the joys of home. Many are the conditions that in modern times threaten the traditional values of home life, but if we are truly grateful for what the homes of our childhood have meant to us, we will never permit those values to be lost. We do well, therefore, on this occasion, to read the following recollections of home life by Kathleen Norris and her admonition to maintain the spiritual values of the traditional American home.

HOW WE USED TO LOVE the very rooms of home when I was a child! We were used to them, we knew them all well, good points and bad. We knew the glowing softness with which winter sunsets crept redly into the hall, we knew just the cracks on the narrow enclosed back stairway where odors of bacon and coffee drifted up on cold mornings. The shadows that the lamp threw on the gracious walls, the spare room where visiting aunts mysteriously unpacked their "telescope baskets," the couch in the window corner of Mother's room, where anyone only moderately invalided was luxuriously installed,—these were not detached externals, they were a part of our very selves.

And back of them was the code of home, and the influence of home. There was prayer for one thing, there were books and games, endless jokes based upon endless absurdities, countless interlocking interests and dependencies. We all have to live among our kind in this world, and it is a sorrowful thing to see how few of us know how to do it, how best to spare each other's sensitive spots and save our own. Home is the place to learn this art; a person who can live in peace at home, who is beloved and necessary at home, can live in peace anywhere, and be beloved and necessary there. Home ought to be our clearing house, the place from which we go forth lessoned and disciplined, and ready for life.

Not to see this, not to see the infinite possibilities that lie behind nursery and school room troubles, is to prove that our generation has its blind eye, as every generation has apparently. . . .

Our generation, in its mad rush for amusements that do not amuse, distractions that leave us duller and more bored than ever, more money, more motors, more travel, more clothes, all destined to blunt our capacity for enjoyment rather than to increase it—we are equally blind.

The building of a Family remains the Great Adventure, the road that is always new. It is not for every man and woman to undertake it; it is a happiness, a fulfilment not granted to all. But ah, the glory and the beauty and the triumph of the dreaded Fifties and Sixties to the man and woman who begin them deeply established in a real home of their own creating!

Home, Sweet Home

'Mid pleasures and palaces though we may roam;
Be it ever so humble, there's no place like home.
A charm from the skies seems to hallow us there
Which, seek through the world, is ne'er met with else-
    where.
Home! Home! sweet, sweet home!
    There's no place like home!
    There's no place like home!

An exile from home, splendor dazzles in vain;
Oh! give me my lowly thatched cottage again!
The birds singing gaily, that come at my call—
Give me them, with the peace of mind dearer than all.
Home! Home! sweet, sweet home!
    There's no place like home!
    There's no place like home!

—John Howard Payne

Thanks for the Blessings of Home

OUR FATHER, to whom we look to make us at
home in this strange and mysterious universe, we
thank Thee on this day of national Thanksgiving for
the blessed homes of America,

325

For the love and affection, the comfort and security, the reverence and holiness that marked the family life of the early generations of our people.

Most of us carry in our hearts some happy memories of the home in which we were born,

> In the shelter of which we learned our first lessons of loyalty, helpfulness, truth, and honor.

May our homes afford us a haven of rest away from the swirling currents of life, a retreat of privacy where we and our families can be ourselves and shut out the clamorous voices that stupefy our feelings, disturb our thinking, and distract our will and purpose.

> May our children find in the home a warm and sheltered nest, where they can grow to wholesome maturity.

But let us not in the comfort of our homes forget the homeless,

> Or those whom human folly and greed have condemned to live in unwholesome hovels or huddled in wretched tenements amidst filth and squalor.

Help us to make America's homes fit abodes for beings created in Thine image,

> Worthy shrines for all that hallows American life.

May our homes, through the sacred memories of our forebears, link us with the past and, through the birth and rearing of children, link us with the future, so that we may know ourselves to be children of the Eternal,

That our lives may ever serve ideals which shall outlive us and shall abide with our posterity when we are no more.

As we thank Thee on this day for the blessed homes of our childhood, so may our children in the days to come have occasion to rejoice in their memories of home and offer Thee thanks and praises for Thy unfailing love. AMEN.

Closing Prayer

O THOU who art our Creator and who sustainest our life by Thy bounties, Thou who hast blessed our land with all manner of wealth, bless Thou also us Thy people with the spirit of humility. Let us not, in the pride of possession, forget that we but hold all this wealth in trust and that only when we are faithful to that trust and use our wealth with wisdom, justice, and generosity can it yield us true happiness. Teach us that the joy of creation far surpasses that of acquisition, that there is more security in mutual helpfulness than in selfish hoarding, that to earn the love and gratitude of our fellow men affords a deeper satisfaction than to force their fear, servility, and envy. We thank Thee, O God, for all Thy gifts, but above all we thank Thee for the gift of Thy spirit, for only by it can we learn to use Thy gifts for our blessing. AMEN.

Temple Israel
Minneapolis, Minnesota

IN HONOR OF THE BAT MITZVAH OF
DAPHNE FRUCHTMAN
FROM
DEENA FRUCHTMAN